I Said, "I Am A Nun"

Choosing excellence in the face of adversity

By

June A. Ramsay

Junearamsay.com

junearamsay@aol.com

Juneology1@gmail.com

Books by June A. Ramsay

By The Riverside

(Magic happens when you follow your haunches)

I Said, "I Am A Nun"

(Choosing excellence in the face of adversity)

Her Father's Sin

(What goes around comes around – A karmic repayment)

Table of Contents

Dedication

I dedicated this book to the memory of my loving mother, Sybil Edna Andrews-Ramsay (1935 – 2007). A woman who deserved a crown for her sacrifices, her leadership, and her example of womanhood, motherhood, and unconditional love. Thank you, Mom!

An inspiring 'faith based' love story of how choosing excellence could lift us above despair to live triumphantly, even when the choices for excellence are difficult and unpopular.

GOD

God made His World so Beautiful

Words cannot describe,

The Plants and Flowers

So many colours, so Beautiful and inspiring.

And Most of all his masterpiece His People, are destroying
His Beautiful World with Hate.

Sybil Edna Ramsay

1935-2007

“Whatever the problem—Love is the answer.”

—*Emmett Fox*

If Love is the answer—and God is Love— then God is the answer!

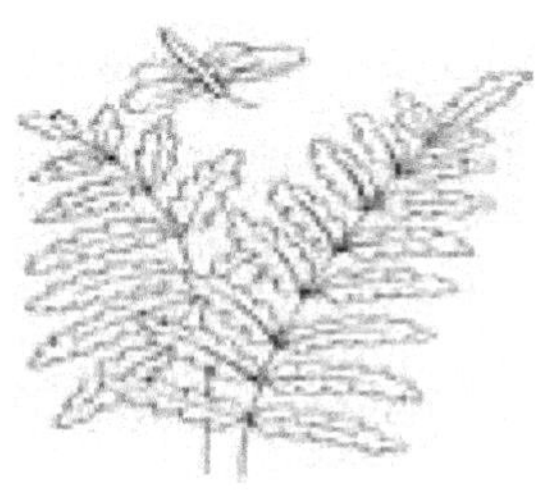

Introduction

For many of us, there is that once-in-a-lifetime experience that defines us. Something happens that changes us profoundly leaving us to prove to ourselves and to the world who and what we really are. Some of us survive extreme situations while others do not. The decisions we make from one moment to the next could be what defines our success or our failure.

In early 1950s, Rose, a small-town Caribbean, Island girl, knew from the tender age of seven she wanted to be a nun to serve God and mankind. She was granted the privilege of attending a convent for training for what she called, 'Her gift to be a presence of God in the world.' But life would have her face many horrific issues, some unthinkable and some unbearable. Rose was wronged.

Rose's broken life had to be placed in a cast to heal. Julia, her confidant, and protector, served as that friend we all need to help us carry our burdens when they sometimes seem too heavy for us to bear.

While healing, Rose accepted her life and the wrong she endured and knew that the wrong could not be undone but had to be forgiven.

After her love of being a nun, she found a second love that was forbidden. That love lived in her heart for decades and gave her the will to keep her focus during her struggles of finding her way through the maze of life.

The passion Rose had for those two loves caused her excruciating pain yet undeniable comfort.

Rose's sacrifices through her lowest points propelled her to reach unbelievable heights of love, forgiveness, success, and happiness beyond her wildest dreams.

After Rose was healed and came out of her cast, she was ready to face life on her terms; she then made a journey back in time to face her opponent in a battle she had to win. Then step by step she designed the life she now wanted, a life of grace and dignity.

It is not what happened to Rose; it was what she did with

what happened to her. She had many opportunities to give up, but instead, she searched for strength deep within herself, going into the silence and listening to that still small voice, and sometimes getting off-the-beaten path to listen—and she heard—with that guidance, she made choices for excellence, unpopular choices from her heart.

Rose's profound journey proved that she knew she was connected to a higher source that was looking out for her and holding her up despite what the world was giving her.

In the end, she had both passions available to her; the first one in a different disguise, and the second one totally available to her without compromise.

This is a story to inspire and encourage you along life's journey, a love story of unquestionable faith and undeniable courage, sprinkled with heartache and romance.

Rose's story is a clear example that when there is a deep desire for anything in your life, you need to keep your focus on it, never let your passion fade away, and never come to the end of your life with your full potential still in you. If Rose had not taken the chances she took, it would be heartbreaking to think of where she could have ended up, especially looking at how and when her life issues started. Through her unpopular choices and sacrifices, she went from bondage to freedom—and from victim to victorious!

And now, a woman of substance! The head of her life. Rose's story will awaken many ranges of emotions in you; from sad to happy, and from mild to severe anger, and then to acceptance and finally joy, unspeakable joy!

Part 1

When More Deception is Not an Option

Sitting by the ocean was the answer for the day. Today, I feel overwhelmed and full of possibilities of what I could or should do with the rest of my life. My soul is thirsty and could only be quenched by the ebb and flow of the ocean waves. As I sat by the ocean, my thoughts wondered on many aspects of my life: where I am, where I could have been, and where I want to be.

My thoughts went on a particular mistake and injustice that happened almost forty years ago. This injustice has devastated my life and shaped it into what it is—and has kept me in silent purgatory. I have kept this mistake and the aspects of it a secret; only sharing the details with my one and only confidant.

About ten minutes into my thoughts, a well-put-together

woman dressed in a business suit came and sat next to me. There were many other places on this boardwalk she could have chosen to sit, but she sat next to me at a distance enough for us to have a conversation. She said, "Hello" and I responded with a "hello" and a smile. "A beautiful day, isn't it?" She spoke. I told her it could not be better.

We spoke about the waves, the boats, and the temperature, and then she asked me what I did and if I worked or lived around the area. I told her, "I am a nun." She looked at me, for I was wearing similar attire to hers, not a nun's attire. She seemed very interested in finding out more about me, and for some reason, I was willing to talk but with some reservations.

"Do you come here often?" She asked. I told her I came on Fridays especially when the cruise ships were in, I love watching the ships and I love the water, so I come as often as possible. It is my way of communing with nature. She asked, "What made you decide to be a nun?" And I told her it is something I knew from about the age of seven, it may have been earlier, but I remembered clearly from that age. I knew with absolute certainty right after I was told about the crucifixion of Christ; I could not see living my life any other way. I wanted to live for him and to serve mankind as he would lead me to serve. She said, "Really, that is wonderful!

I just had my fiftieth birthday, and I still do not know what I want to be when I grow up."

I told her, "It is never too late to decide on something particular—and maybe you are doing what you were meant to do and just do not know that you are. It is just that some of us are led in more specific ways than others. I recently heard a famous author say, 'If you are not sure what it is you want to do with your life, you should think back to when you were about the age of eight or nine and remember what you enjoyed doing, and that is your answer.' For some of us, we have dreams, but some decisions—twists and turns of life, or mistakes can lead us in different directions—leaving us to make the best of what we have left with our lives, or just deal with the hand life has dealt us; sometimes in regret and sometimes in purgatory, like me. I told you I am a nun, but sometimes I feel my life has been pure purgatory."

In quiet desperation, I wished she were an angel because I felt for the first time in decades, to tell the truth about my life and release the secrets that have kept me burdened.

If she were an angel and I confided in her, she would disappear, and I would be fine.

"Prior to being a nun, as I said, I am, and through all these years, I have gone to confessions and know in my heart God has forgiven me for all I have done. But I live in silent purgatory and go through bouts of questioning myself occasionally. Thinking I should have done this, or I should have said that, and this goes on and on, and maybe I could still do or say something, and maybe I will one day. But the one true love and desire to be a nun never wavered; that I am, that is in my heart, in my being.

Life is a combination of decisions, some good and some not so-good, and each choice has its repercussions. At this moment, the decisions we are making will bear fruit bountifully in due season so hopefully, we are sowing good seeds. Also, this moment is the result of many decisions made in the past. I have a friend, Rose, who also wanted to be a nun, she went away to a convent, but dropped out and got married instead and has lived a remarkably interesting and sometimes complicated life.

She brought a lot to the surface recently about the twists and turns her life took, and I often wondered what her life would have been like if she had not made the choices she made; or if the things that happened to her did not happen. Her life consumes and inspires mine at the same time. There is something about you that reminds me of her, I feel like I am looking at her when I look at you. What do you do?" I asked.

She said, “I am an entrepreneur, and my name is Vanessa. I am also an encourager. I see the best in people, and I encourage them on their life’s journey, sometimes helping them to see a clear path for their lives.” I said, “You do have a calling to which you have answered.” She asked me what my name was, and I said, “My name is Julia” and I continued talking.

“Recently I was wondering what would happen if I told the true story of my life and the secrets I am keeping. How shocked would people be, and how would they respond? For many years I wondered about that but never put it to the test, I went around it by telling different stories, stories I wished were true, or stories that mirrored the person asking the question.

You see, I grew up in a home with a father who loved to drink and socialize at the expense of neglecting me, and I learned many coping skills because of that. One was how to paint a beautiful picture of what I wished my life were. So, I told people what I wished, and I moved on. I could create places to go for shelter in my imagination; I am like a turtle, if I feel uncomfortable or threatened about anything I go into my shell, that shell is in my imagination. This has protected me from being judged or having to explain anything I did not want to answer." Then I thought to myself...

Vanessa seemed so free if I could just share my story with her. What a relief it would be for me to unload this burden. I have carried it for all these years, and I do not want to carry it to my grave.

In my mind, I wondered what would happen if I opened to her and she was not an angel but a gossiper who worked in the same area where I worked—maybe in the same building as my office—then these secrets could be out in the open and I am not ready to deal with my life that way. These secrets are not just mine, but they would be a betrayal to my best friend, Rose, whom I have always protected; and I am the only one she has confided in. I would tell her to meet me here again next Friday, and if she comes, I will feel I can trust her, and then I would think about sharing my story with her. I am tired of keeping so much inside; I am ready to release this burden.

The Next Friday

Today, I am a bit anxious with positive anticipation to see Vanessa, today. I asked her to meet me here today. I do not know much about her, but I feel I know her. I feel a connection to her and would like to see her again. Maybe she really was an angel and has disappeared or moved on to another assignment. Perhaps I missed the opportunity to share my story and never have to worry about it getting out there in the wrong way. But why do I want to share my story with her? Who is this woman, who is this stranger?

The cruise ships were in, and the weather was delightful. I sat there thinking about Vanessa and the moment at hand and was wondering if she would show up. My thoughts went on my life and the life of my best friend, Rose, and on the things, we experienced; the twists and turns life took at so many junctures; these thoughts were overwhelming because Rose and I recently spent a lot of time on a European cruise reuniting and facing our truths. On that cruise, a lifetime of secrets was revealed, and that is why I want to share. I want to share with someone who has a certain maturity, and I am hoping Vanessa is the one. I felt comfortable with her… and in that moment I decided to take a walk—the direction did not matter.

My walk brought me to the entrance of the water taxi, and something in me said, "*Go for a ride and be on the water.*" Before thinking through the process, I went on the Water Taxi that had just arrived and was loading up to return to its next trip, wow, I am on the water going for a water ride, how splendid!

When I got back to my point of departure, about twenty minutes later, I was feeling relaxed, composed, and peaceful. I walked back to my spot and sat thinking that I may have missed the opportunity to see my friend, Vanessa. Maybe she came and left in that window of time. Well, if that is the case, maybe I need to let this desire to share go back to rest. After sitting there for a while and almost beginning to feel like I had spent enough time on the water, I was getting ready to walk back to my office; and at that moment, I saw Vanessa coming toward me looking excited to see me. As she got closer, she yelled, "I'm so glad you are here, I was tied up closing out on a project and thought I would miss my opportunity to see you." By that time, she was at the spot with me took her seat, and asked, "How are you?" I said, "Very well, I was testy earlier but went for a ride on the water, and now I am good." After some chitchat about the last week, I told her I was looking forward to seeing her. Then thinking to myself… *this is an opportunity to share, Vanessa did come back, and there is something angelic and trusting about her. I felt the need to release this burden, but, where and how do I start?* I looked at Vanessa and she said, "Your secret is safe with me."

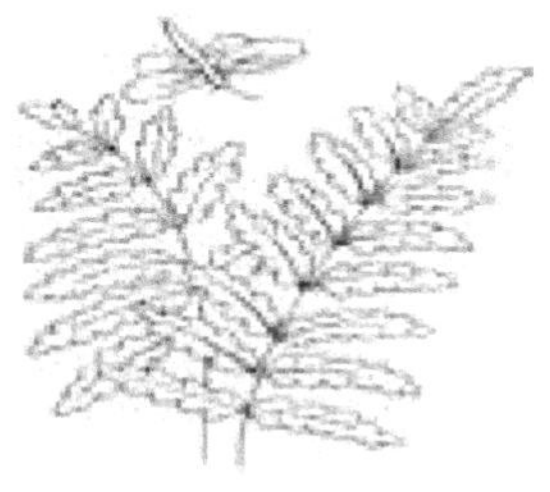

Sharing Confidences—Trusting A Stranger

"My dad was a functioning alcoholic while I was growing up, and that caused many issues in my childhood. He never missed a day of work, yet he drank about every other day that I could remember. His drinking led to many difficulties in my life, including neglect of me and my mom.

He took care of us financially the best way he could, but his drinking, though not the first in his life, was extremely important and sometimes took center stage. Drinking was the norm for most men in our society, it was a cultural thing. A pub was located on almost every corner for people to mind their Pints and Quarts, as they say, 'Minding the P's and Q's.'

As a child, I was never hugged or told I was loved, or that I was special, never by my dad. My mother did not do much hugging either, but she showed me affection in the way she cared for me. Then in her later years, she said the ultimate words to me, many times, "I love you." My mother—a very dutiful woman, a great homemaker, dependable and creative, and took great care of me.

The home situation with my father's drinking contributed to me going into silence and learning to bottle the hurt deep within. There was no proper outlet for the issues I felt so, I learned to create places in my imagination to go for comfort, I called this my 'turtle's shell' and in that shell, *no one* could reach or hurt me. That is how I learned to cope then, and that is how I still cope.

Coupled with those issues, I have a learning disability, I am dyslexic; and certain ways of learning did not work effectively for me. Through my struggles, I did my best to hide my disability and learned how to function and maintain my grades. School was hard because I had to read everything three or four times before I understood, and I had to recheck everything I wrote, especially numbers. I naturally wrote backward and transposed numbers, so I had to be conscious of writing correctly.

From an early age, I wanted to help people, maybe as a teacher. And since my teachers were nuns, I felt gravitated to that calling. As a child, I did not know much about the depths of that calling; but Rose and I would pretend to be imaginary nuns when we played and would daydream of being the best nuns helping lots of people everywhere. Not knowing that soon after having those wishes I would be exposed to the depth of that calling."

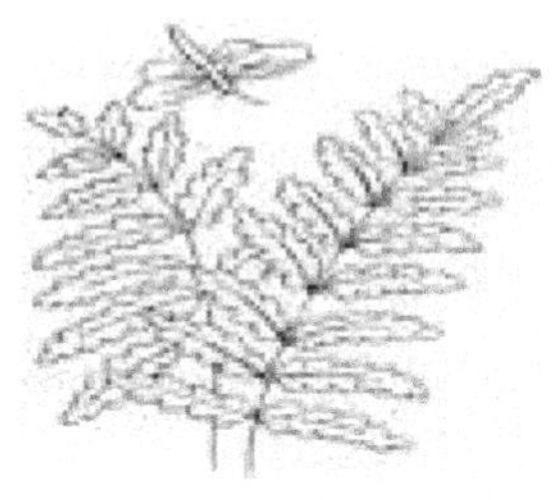

What I Knew at Age Seven

It is not often that children at the age of seven know what they want to do the next day, much less for their lives. I was born into a family where people were scared to take chances and only made the decisions that would give them comfortable results right where they were. No one took a chance on anything. They all lived in the comfort zone they found themselves in with much complaint but would never make any decision to get out. It bothered and annoyed me, and I can remember looking at the way they were so scared to move in a different direction to try something out of the ordinary. All the opportunities were elsewhere, but they would sit around and just be. I remembered listening to stories of other people leaving our town or the island and venturing on to betterment and then hearing of their success—but not any of my family, any success for them would have to come to them where they were.

One day I wanted to see people move and wondered if they had to move, where would they go? I went to school, and they were there; I came home, and they were there, doing the same thing every day. I was around the age of six, and in my six-year-old mind, I decided to burn the house down, my grandfather's old house where everyone lived including me. It was about a year after that when my parents bought a home with a large orchard in the country, and we moved. However, I started a fire in the basement where there was a stove and I was alone, all the adults were on the patio doing their usual lamenting and complaining. I started the fire, and it was soon blazing and expanding, I got confused and decided to use all I could find to cover it. At my disposal were lots of old newspapers that I used to cover the fire, but the fire kept burning through the paper, and there was a lot of smoke that caused the fire alarm to go off and for me to get caught. To my misfortune, the fire was discovered, and fortunately put out without burning the house down or with much damage. I got in trouble for doing that and was punished for not doing anything like that again. From what I saw in those tender years, I decided I would make decisions without fear and go wherever I needed to go to find opportunities. I was fearless about life then, and I still am now.

The Easter of my seventh birthday, I went to Sunday school. A beautiful Sunday with a few friends from the neighborhood. This day was memorable. It was the week before Easter, Palm Sunday, and the subject being taught was the history of Easter. We sat in the rectory of the church where Sunday school was held. I was wearing my most beautiful cotton (floral print), navy background with light pink and white flowers with a white collar that was hand embroidered. I had coordinating socks, and my Mary Jane shoes to match. My pocketbook was black patent leather with a rose closure and short handles, which contained my hand-embroidered cotton handkerchief and my weekly offering to give at offering time. All my friends were dressed similarly. The teachers were people I liked, and there were about three of them in attendance.

That day, of all the other days, I must have been paying attention, or something came alive in me. My teacher spoke about the crucifixion. I had not heard about that before, not that I remembered, but the way she spoke about Jesus and this crucifixion was like something magnificent, I was like a sponge soaking up the next drop of water. I knew Jesus. I was taught about Jesus by my mother, and I prayed to him each night and each morning. My mom told me that Jesus loved me so much, he would never leave me or forsake me! He was my invisible best friend, a friend who loved me and would always be with me. I spoke to him in my 'turtle's shell' all the time, but more often when I was afraid, and I had one other friend I allowed in the 'turtle's shell,' Rose. Each morning and night I enjoyed saying my prayers:

Morning

Now I wake and see the light
God has kept me through the night.
Keep me safe, oh Lord, I pray
Keep and guide me through this day.
Amen

Evening

This night as I lay down to sleep
I gave you, Lord, my soul to keep
If I should die before I wake
I gave you, Lord, my soul to take.
In my bed I lie,
Heavenly Father,
hear my cry.
Lord, protect me through the night,
And bring me safe to morning's light.
Amen

How I loved those prayers, there is a sweet innocence in them that brings me to a childlike state. I have told them every day of my life and have taught them to every child I have had an opportunity to teach. I tell them all the time, sometimes with more meaning than others. But at seven years of age, they were the most special things I had, and there is still something special about saying them now.

The day I learned about this other aspect of my Jesus was confusing. I could not understand that He died, and yet He was still alive. I did not understand that He rose again since that was not revealed until later in the class.

I had a difficult time understanding a crucifixion, and that it means death. I thought it was something special or a big-word adults use but, I learned that day what it was, and it horrified me, broke my heart, and changed me profoundly.

In that instant, I became very serious about life and was angry at the people who crucified my Jesus. I did not know about hate, but that had to be my first feeling of severe dislike toward others, to those who had done this to my Jesus.

Looking back, I feel I was too young for the exposure I had that day. I was not mentally ready for it, I think it tampered with some of my development where I have grown into a deeper introvert and have been very serious, sometimes too serious about life. I treasure the moments when I can be alone at the end of the day or on my weekends. Those moments are special to me and anyone or anything getting in the way becomes the enemy. I think my quiet time is what completes me. Another person or thing cannot do it for me.

Jesus suffered for me! I felt an immediate difference in my heart that has not changed to this day. That difference is profoundly felt each Easter. Easter and Christmas are very important to me. I cry each Easter; I do all I can to honor the meaning of that profound act of human kindness that was displayed by God to mankind so long ago.

That day I cried helplessly. My beautiful handkerchief could not hold my tears. Those were tears from my heart. I flooded the classroom. I felt profound pain, and nothing could comfort me. My teacher tried to coax and comfort me, the other teachers came to assist, but to no avail. That was my first profound feeling of loss, pain, and sadness. In that moment I knew I wanted to help Jesus. I wanted to be with Him, I wanted to see Him. However, it was going to be done, I wanted Him in my life all the time. I did not know what people did to work for Him, but I wanted to do whatever that was for Him.

One of the teachers, after listening to my sobbing and

trying to comfort me said, "But, He is alive now, He rose from the dead!" That was more confusing. I understood that something could die, and it must be buried because one of my friends had lost her dog, and her dad kept a funeral for it in the backyard of their home. I understood that the dog would not be coming back. I saw them put him in a box and bury him deep in the earth. So, when the teacher told me that Jesus was alive, I was more confused, her efforts to comfort me were a good attempt at stopping the tears and made me want to listen. After some moments, I was taken to a quiet place in the church where she explained the resurrection. I do not know if I believed or understood totally at the time. But what she explained to me stopped my tears and left me wanting to know more. I went home as a different child from the one who left home hoping and skipping hours earlier.

On my return home, I did not remember any of my friends although we walked together. I was in my own world, a world of confusion, pain, and disappointment. My teacher walked behind us and came to my mom to explain what had happened and the experience I had. I remembered my mother giving me cookies and ice cream, which was the usual treat after Sunday school, and then giving me a bath and putting me in bed early. The sun was still up, and I never went to bed while the sun was still shining, but I did that day. We were out of school for

Easter week, and I had moments to relive that experience without interruption. When my friends came to play, I was not interested in the trivial things we did anymore. I was in disbelief for what was a life change, I was not the same anymore.

Going forward, I decided to be the best little girl there was. Every teacher loved me. I knew that my life would be doing something for my Jesus, working for him, being good in general, being kind to people, and helping them. I wanted to be a presence that reminded people of God in the world, to do the things He would be proud of and do them in the way He would approve, and for me, that was being a nun and teaching. It was about this time that I started understanding what nuns really were and that all of them were not teachers. I gravitated to all the good things as I understood what was good. I looked at the adults around me and saw their confusion and could not understand why they were making the choices they made or were not making.

A few years passed, and I was about nine going on ten years of age, people would constantly say this child has an 'old head.' The young people around never held my interest, they annoyed me with the things that interest them, and I felt I was ahead of my own time—maybe I was too serious about life. I had no interest in participating in the things children my age was involved in. I wanted quiet time whenever possible so I could think about my Jesus and be with him uninterrupted at every opportunity I had. Being in that quiet brought me joy, joy, and peace I never found elsewhere. I was not a sad child as the picture would sometimes seem, I was happy in my own way. But as a child, I had to do what the grown-ups wanted me to do, I could not make my own decisions, so on numerous occasions, I had to attend some of those functions that I saw as a waste of time and energy. But they were all part of the growing pains and development I needed.

Each night I would curl up in bed and could not wait for that quiet time just before going off to sleep when the lights went off so I could pray and spend that special time with Jesus. It was so precious and special. I was able to differentiate what I knew from what I believed. And I knew at that age, I wanted to always be in God's good graces. I knew I wanted to do only what would make Him happy. There was something in my heart that only I could feel, and it was profound, I had much difficulty discussing and trying to explain it to my friends—no one understood. I knew then that I could never be sad about anything unless I left Jesus out. He lived in my heart, and no one or nothing could move him. Everything could be moved away from me but not Him.

By the age of eleven, I was living a life that made me happy, going to church on Sunday mornings with my mom, then Sunday school in the afternoons with my friends, and enjoying each moment of being at church because that was being in the presence of God. At that age, I was confirmed into the Anglican Church. The most popular religion on my Island. The occasion was grand! I wore the traditional white lace dress with all the frills and fuss, and all the people in my life were there cheering me on. Then my First Communion was a step closer to the life I wanted.

My heart would go out to any nun I saw, in my heart they were 'earth angels' who were here to assist God and work on His behalf. I wanted to be a nun more than I wanted my next breath. During that phase of my life, I was incredibly involved in the church. The church had lots of activities during the year, and I would be at every activity as those were the things that had meaning in my life.

The school I attended was a church school linked to the Church of England. One day it was announced that the Queen was coming to visit, and the school and church combined were doing things in her honor. I was selected to be part of the greeting party. I was elated! A few of my other friends were also selected. I could hardly wait to get home to tell my parents. I was so happy, and they were too.

The time came, and after meeting and greeting the Queen, I was part of the group that danced for her at our City Hall, which was one of the finest buildings in our city. I did my duty well with honor and respect. After those two major events in the eleventh year of my life, I started unconsciously pulling adults to me who saw my potential. I had no difficulty expressing what it was I wanted to do with my life. I wanted to attend a convent high school instead of a regular high school for my training and development to be a nun.

My life was one of love, respect, and admiration from all the older people around my home, neighborhood, and school. I grew up where it took a village to raise a child, and my village was proud of its product. I was blossoming into a lovely young lady and had chosen a pleasing direction for my life, and I had the total support of all my elders.

There was one young lady, Mary Anne, a neighbor of my grandmother who had gone abroad to seek a nun’s life, and at that time in my life, she was the one person I was most interested in hearing about. She was a presence in the world that reminded the world of God. She visited home one summer and wore her nun's habit, and I could not take my eyes off her. I remembered her as a regular girl attending high school and being around, then to see her come back from the convent ordained and wearing her nun's attire was astonishing to me. That served as more confirmation of what I really wanted to do with my life. I had seen many nuns but never knew any of them. Mary Anne would send pictures to her mom, whom I adored, and her mom would share those pictures with me. Her mom was also one of my favorite people, I loved hanging around her. She was my grandmother's friend. She was dignified and beautiful and was married and had other children besides Mary Anne. She had the most beautiful home and garden. I spent time with her when she worked in her garden and when she sewed and played the piano. She taught me a lot of those skills. I developed a great interest in sewing and gardening through her. And throughout my life, sewing and gardening have remained my favorite hobbies. Whenever I was off from school, I would be with her, shadowing her in all she did. She loved me. She called me her 'little old friend'. One day she said to my grandmother, "This is a special child, she has an extraordinary personality for her age and a gentle soul that will go very far in life touching other lives." I never forgot those words. She knew what I wanted to do. She knew I wanted to be like her daughter, in service at home or abroad, I did not care where; I just wanted to serve.

The time was closely approaching for me to attend high school, and my parents had to be convinced about my choice to attend a neighboring convent to gain my high school education and get a taste of convent life. During that time, I would daydream about the convent, and then one weekend my dad took us for a drive to see the convent's location and surroundings. This was about one hour's drive from our home. I was in heaven 'on earth.' Everything fascinated me, I wanted to be there so badly that I prayed every second for my parents to allow me to attend this convent. It took a lot of convincing from the convent, my grandmother's friend, some church officials, and my schoolteachers for my parents to consider this step in my life. My parents were concerned about my age and allowed me to be away from home.

After months of serious talking and lecturing to me about life, revisiting discussions with the convent, and rechecking the facilities, they gave their approval. I was elated! My life was as complete as it could be, and I knew that all the lectures my parents gave would not go in vain. They would be proud, I was going to serve the Lord, I was going to continue being that good child focusing on working hard for God, and I was going to be a presence of God in the world. I was happy!

My parents and I prepared for my send-off to convent, and

it was joy untouchable. I could not be happier. I had a great summer and left my friends who were off to high school, along with my known neighborhood to start a new life with a new focus. And that was the inauguration of my life's issues.

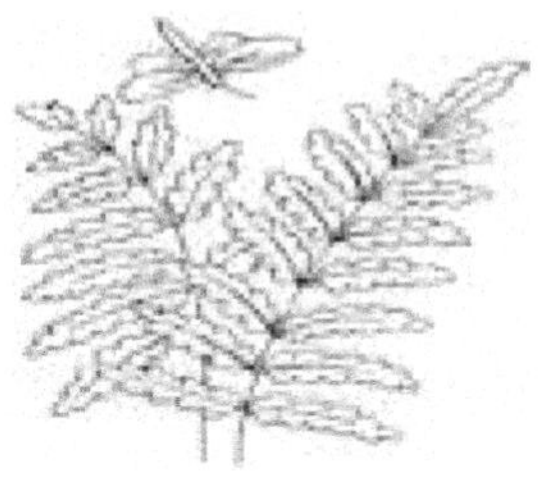

The Convent

At the age of thirteen plus, Rose and I started convent life to gain our high school education and focus on becoming nuns. Rose was my best friend from as far back as I can remember. We grew up together. She and her parents resided next door to us. While at the convent, we spent a lot of time getting to know ourselves and each other better and observing all the teachings while loving our lives as nuns in training. We were happy being on the path that was destined for us.

After completion of the first year in the convent, we were invited to be part of the audience to witness the ceremony where the nuns took their first 'Profession of Faith' vows.

After those first vows, the nuns lived a consecrated life for two years. At the end of those two years of living out their Profession of Faith, they took their second vows, the 'Sacrifice of Obedience.' This lasted for five years—then the final vows are taken at the end of that fifth year.

From the first vows to the final vows are a total of seven years. The seven years allowed the nuns to live a life of poverty, chastity, and obedience—a consecrated life—and to utterly understand the life they have chosen; this was the time to reflect and know for sure if this is what they really want.

The first ceremony, the Profession of Faith, was an engagement celebration; an engagement that lasted for seven years before the final (marriage) vows were taken. Taking the final vows was a grand ceremony equal to that of a wedding. We saw this in class on video tape. Nuns are identified as '*Brides of Christ.*' Some nuns wore a wedding band from that day forth; they dressed as brides for this grand occasion. These are real marriage vows—the nun is the bride, and Jesus Christ is the Groom. At the ceremony, the bride's face is covered, and she lays prostrate on the altar with her face to the ground in the presence of the archbishop, the Abbess, and all in attendance. Laying on the altar is a sign of laying down her life in service to God. Then, they sign the 'Book of Nuns' at the altar sealing their promise of poverty, chastity, and obedience. They signed while on their knees. After that, the Abbess signs. The archbishop then blesses the nuns to the vocation and the final vows are recited: "*Till Death Do We*

Meet." At that time, their faces are shown.

We had the opportunity to attend the first ceremony, the 'Profession of Faith.' This was a profound and positive experience; it was life-empowering and electrifying. After the ceremony, there was a reception with a cake that was the equivalent of a wedding cake, and the new nuns who had just professed their faith cut and shared with all in attendance. It was an awesome experience and valuable exposure for us interested in that calling. After the ceremony, some of the nuns connected with us to take us under their wings to be our mentors. We could not be happier.

A few months after attending the 'Profession of Faith' ceremony something unexpected happened.

One ordinary Sunday evening during roll call, Rose was absent. She did not return to the convent on time; this was unusual for her since she was always so excited about getting back after our weekends away. Shortly before joining the convent, we met some new friends who had moved to our neighborhood, one of them was older and gave us genuine advice about the expected adventures at hand, leaving home and being away from all we knew would not be easy. This new friend had already completed university studies and had a lot of good advice for us, and on our weekends off from the convent, we socialized and went to different activities with our friends. That night in question, Rose and I separated as we were returning to the convent.

I went back to the convent earlier with a few friends who were heading in that direction. Rose was left with a few other friends including our older friend.

When we started our studies at the convent, we were told that this time of training, and at our age, was not for seclusion and confinement; it was for education first, and a clear understanding of what we might be choosing. So, it was acceptable for us to have friends and socialize.

The evening in question was late, and still Rose was not back. We retired to pray and rest. On awakening the next morning, Rose was there at breakfast. On our way to class, I tried to find out what happened, but she did not say much, but something was gruesomely wrong. Rose was distraught and distant with a few scratches on one side of her face, her eyes puffed from leftover tears. She said, "I will talk later, I had an accident, the Abbess and my parents know about it." We kept on moving to class, and the day kept rolling on while Rose was excused to rest.

Months later, we were getting ready to celebrate our fifteenth birthday, and I was excited! Rose was suffering from asthma, something she had suffered violently as a child from birth to about ten years of age, and it was affecting her again. As a child, she was so ill, that her parents thought she would die on many occasions. Now the asthma symptoms were taking over again. Her breathing was difficult and visibly laborious.

During this time, Rose was more dedicated to her calling and refused to take any time off to go home; not even for a few hours to meet our friends on the weekends. She was happy at the convent; I was too, we never left in the months after that night she was late getting back. I wanted to know what happened, but she always said she was 'okay' and trying to manage how she was feeling, and that the asthma medication made her very tired. I knew there was more. I just knew . . .

Rose was not getting better. One night, she became so ill she had to be hospitalized. But in a few days with increased medication and time away from classes seemed to help.

We had our fifteenth birthday celebration, and it was not much fun for Rose. Although she was getting better, the Abbess was not happy with her lack of zest and insisted she see a doctor for more tests to understand what was happening. After the results came in, the doctor said some tests would take a few more days to come back, but as of now, there is nothing he can see beyond the flare-up of asthma, and for her to keep taking the medication and rest. A couple more weeks went by, and Rose was not improving as expected, so her parents were called in for permission to run further tests as she was still a minor. They gave permission, and the tests were conducted.

When the new test results came in, her parents were asked to attend a meeting with the doctor. The Abbess wanted to attend but decided to let Rose, her parents, and the doctor have their discussion privately. The Abbess was on standby, praying for Rose.

In a very matter-of-fact way, the doctor said to Rose, "These tests confirm that you are pregnant!" There was a long, loud silence . . .

The sweet hum of her life was hushed.

Rose literally died that day! Her parents started questioning her because they were shocked and wanted to know who was responsible for this. "Could the tests be wrong? Was it someone at the convent facility, a visitor? How did this happen? Who did this?" The pressure of what Rose was faced with and in the presence of the most important people in her life, she fainted!

Rose woke up the following morning with her mom at her

bedside. She said to her mom, "I am sorry." Her mom decided not to burden her further with questions because she saw the pressure her child was under, but asked her, "Who did this?" Rose told her mom who was responsible.

A meeting was scheduled with her parents and the Abbess to discuss what would be the next steps in this catastrophe. Of course, there was only one thing that could happen now - Rose had to leave the convent. Fifteen years old and three months pregnant!

Dishonor, embarrassment, shame, disgrace, confusion, and the death of a special dream were some of the feelings that consumed Rose. How would she look up again? And look up to what? The one request she had was for the opportunity to leave quietly and not tell anyone 'Why' until she was gone. The Abbess said, "Your wish would be granted." She hugged Rose and blessed her.

A Change in Direction

The Day Rose Left the Convent

A very sad Friday evening, even the universe was sad and showed its disapproval with a fierce thunderstorm. Rose said goodbye to a few friends, saying she had to leave because of a situation she got involved in.

Good-bye to her dreams, her education, and the life she wanted more than anything else. She never told anyone what happened that night in question, but I knew. I just knew – I could feel it to my bones.

Rose packed her few things while the Abbess kept her company, trying to console her with kind words of encouragement. Saying maybe God had a different plan for your life, not to serve as a nun, but as a mother. Rose cried enough tears to fill a river and then some. But it was not only the tears that were being shed; it was the injustice that she kept inside. The painful secret of that night.

The day Rose left the convent. She started serving a life sentence for becoming a mother instead of a nun. Life as she knew it would never be the same again.

The torture started the next day as she went home to her neighborhood. With the neighbors and the scandal and gossip, she could not sleep, she could not think, the tears kept flowing, and she was angry at the person who did this to her.

We did not communicate much during this time as I went away to continue my training at a different facility. She lived out her pregnancy in isolation and was judged by all who knew her, some parents who had daughters her age kept their daughters away from her. She was looked on as a bad influence.

Even the boyfriend, the older friend, and the father of the baby neglected her out of fear. He tried to visit her during the pregnancy, but she did not talk to him. She was neglected by all the outside sources she had known at that time in her life. Rose went from the product of goodness to one of disgrace.

Rose hid away on her parents' property, which was conducive to hiding. The property was enclosed with a tall fence and large trees surrounding the inside of the fence. The property had many fruit trees and different areas of herbal gardens. Some sections were reserved for rearing chickens and ducks. There was also a fishpond. It was a beautiful country orchard. She stayed in that orchard and cared for the plants, day after day, a way of redirecting her energies, away from the view of everyone; and she read every book she had from school and everything her parents had in their home. This was a time when Rose should have been developing her intellectual abilities, improving her social skills and consciousness, and gaining her education and training. However, our society did not allow pregnant girls to attend school, so she could not attend any school on our Island; it was against the law. Rose was in an invisible prison.

The combination of the stress on her young body, the shame she endured, the embarrassment of having to leave the convent that she so loved, and the disappointment she brought to her parents, caused her to go give birth stressfully to a that baby who had a fifty-fifty chance of survival.

The delivery was overly complicated, and Rose had serious surgery immediately after the birth of the baby and was placed in intensive care, followed by being on a critical watch list. Rose did not want to live and had no desire to get better. She was hospitalized for a while before returning home with the baby who was also in intensive care because of its premature birth. Rose vowed that she would never be in such a situation again—never.

During that crucial time in the hospital, there were droves of girls from her neighborhood who would leave school on their lunch hour and go to the hospital to see if they could see Rose. The hospital kept them away, but those girls were trying daily to get into the hospital to see her.

The visitation from the boyfriend really did not happen, so the baby was three weeks old before he found out about its birth and Rose's condition.

Two months later, Rose and her baby were discharged from the hospital. She was feeling better and glad to have her body back to herself, she did not enjoy being pregnant, it was an invasion of her body and her life. Now home from the hospital, it was different, and there were contemporary issues to deal with; the baby and its needs, and the turmoil she was going through emotionally. Rose did not want to breastfeed the baby; she hated it. She wanted to use baby formula, but her mom would not let her. Still a minor she had to listen to her mom; also, Rose had no income and no way of providing for herself. In those moments and many other similar moments, she made vows to herself about what she would do one day; she just had to hang on.

Part 2

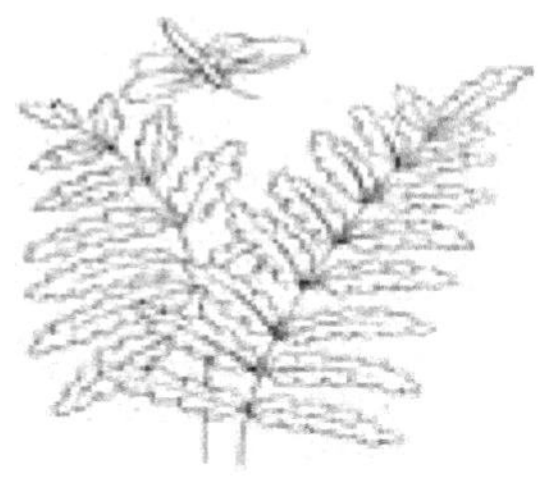

The Reunion—A Release from Invisible Bondage

Vanessa and I decided to hang out on the waterfront for the rest of the afternoon, she was deeply interested in hearing my story and that of my best friend, Rose. I can hardly wait to share what took place on a recent cruise with Rose. A reunion out of this world!

For all my life, as far back as I can remember, Rose and I communicated regularly, sometimes in-depth and sometimes just on the surface; she recently insisted we go on a cruise to put things in perspective.

The cruise was sharing and revealing the details of the past; the night of her getting back to the convent late, and all that was buried deep in her subconscious and in her 'turtle's, shell.' Rose came to the surface and the truth was revealed. The 'turtle's shell' was cracked open.

Rose spoke of everything in chronological order of how and when they occurred, and she could not stop talking. She needed to set herself free, and so did I.

Rose's Story

Rose Speaking to Julia…

Julia, I want to finally put these secrets of my life to rest. This trip is about freedom, setting myself free. I want to heal; I want out of this purgatory. I want to bring the truth to the surface once and for all.

The night I was late coming back to the convent, and the day I left the convent, the beautiful hum of my life was muted—in an instant.

I was in a daze of disbelief. I went from the highest high to the lowest low in my life. I experienced emotions I did not understand, and the confusion of my life kept me at a loss. I think many times when I went to sleep, I had passed out of consciousness, and with no schedule to keep I would wake up or come through in my own time. I felt I was sometimes living outside of myself and looked forward to going to sleep to escape what was happening. I was trying to find myself and could not, then there was this horrible reality of something growing inside of me and I could not escape it. I was trapped in a hell I would wish on no one.

The Delivery

The day of the delivery was a long day; I ended up in the hospital unexpectedly because I was not feeling well and was left to see a doctor. The delivery came quickly, and I gave birth alone in the poorest part of the hospital, the part that was government provision for the homeless and the outcasts. My parents had no idea I would be delivering the baby at that time because it was not time. I was in a different part of the hospital to see a doctor for a check-up to be sure everything was okay. Unfortunately, I went into labor and did not have the proper paperwork or insurance since I was a minor and did not have anything, it would be my parent's insurance that would cover me, and they were not there at the time. All I had was an identification card and a few pennies; so, I was immediately sent to the area for paupers.

On that delivery bed, in a place that must be close to what hell looks like—I delivered my baby alone.

Shortly after delivering my baby, I was placed on a small cot, the smallest size bed, where I lay and thought of how alone I was. I had no voice and at that moment, no one. In that instant, at the age of fifteen, I made a promise to myself that I would never, under any condition, be in this situation again.

Laying in that bed and thinking about the agonizing pregnancy and the horrendous delivery I had just gone through; I could not imagine how much pain I was feeling. It was the feeling of wanting to faint and wishing to die. Then thinking I now had another person I was totally responsible for, I did not want this life, no part of me wanted it.

Whatever my condition was—I passed out and a few of the women around me called for the nurses who I understood took their own time in responding to the call (since this area was for the outcasts of society) and when they finally did, I had to be rush to the emergency room for immediate surgery to save my life. I wish the nurses did not respond.

By the time my parents came to get me, they found out I had already delivered the baby under emergency conditions, and I was in emergency surgery. The complications from the delivery and the surgery kept me in the hospital for an extended period, and the baby had to remain in the hospital in an incubator to gain some weight and for warmth and observation.

I awakened to a new set of responsibilities I did not want and literally resented.

It was eight months after the birth of my baby before I came up for air. Being cut off from the convent, my high school education, and my friends was very difficult; in addition to the way people judged and rejected me. It was as if I were contagious. People did not want their daughters around me. I lost faith and trust in people. No one knew what happened because I never told my story, but I was judged. And I did not tell my story because I feared being judged, condemned, and cast aside in another way. It was said that I had taken the steps of an adult, and I was expected to act like one.

A few months after the birth of my baby, my parents pressured the baby's father to marry me. With him not being sure of what I had disclosed to them, he decided to marry me. And soon the news came out that I was getting married. And I did.

Marriage

The boyfriend, who was not around for the birth of the baby, was making every attempt to get involved.

This was a time when people did not have telephones in their homes, except for the 'well to do.' So, gossip was the way word got around, word of mouth – in the streets, everyone had an opinion. Rose's community was very active in her life and affairs.

The community played a role in everything in the Caribbean in the early 1950s. The unofficial community leaders had a say in how things should go. So, under the pressure of the community, my parents broke their silence and revealed the name of the boyfriend. Then the pressure of the community on the boyfriend and the pressure from my parents collectively, he decided he wanted to get married.

The gossip was overwhelming. People were up and down the streets, from house to house...

He knew that marrying me was better than the alternative. This marriage, though wrong, would give me what everyone thought was right—a name, a home, and a provider, and two parents for the new baby. But that was the last thing I wanted; however, again, I had no voice, I was still a minor, and I had messed up and disappointed my parents when they trusted me and gave in to what I said I wanted so badly. So, I could not have a say now.

The wedding plans started. My mom was happy planning it and I went along as I was supposed to. She deserved that happiness after the disgrace I caused her. I had a beautiful dress of pure white bridal satin trimmed with bridal white lace that was made by my grandmother's friend, my favorite person. I was allowed to do a few things on it, but I was not enthusiastic at the least, but I went along as I was expected to. The day of the wedding was a splendid Saturday afternoon in the middle of summer, a beautiful day for my society and my proud parents.

I got dressed at my favorite lady's home. She was delighted to have me dress at her home, a place I loved very much, and I allowed her that happiness. When my dad came to get me for us to go to the church, there was a crowd of people waiting at the gate and on the street to have a glimpse of me. Word had gotten around of the location where I was dressing to leave for the ceremony. On the way to the church about a block away I could not believe the droves of people I saw walking and some running toward the church and around that area; I wondered what was happening, but as we turned on the street of the church there were no more questions of what was happening, the crowd was there to see me. My dad held my hand as we entered the church, and I kept my eyes focused straight ahead. Many people were fighting to get to the front of the crowd, and I heard a few people saying, "We love you, Rose" and before long there was a momentum of people humming "we love you, Rose; we love you, Rose!" I got emotional in those moments but kept my focus. As we got into the church and went from one level of confusion on the outside of the church to the sound of awe . . . on the inside. Then the sound of everyone rising to their feet at the same time, and the bridal music for me to walk to the altar played, it was like I was not there, I turned off all my feelings and emotions. Everyone was happy except me. The bridal party followed and as I was walking down the aisle, I noticed my Abbess and a few nuns; I recognized two of them who had taken their vows and had gravitated to me as my mentors. I could not smile - I nodded my head in recognition.

The ceremony was a nice one that I could not enjoy, the church was beautifully decorated with flowers and candles, and I wept at the altar, I was a weeping bride. I wept because I was taking the wrong vows to the wrong person.

The reception was grand, and I sat at the bride's table and accepted well wishes from all who were in attendance. My Abbess came to my table and prayed with me then she gave me a gift, a beautiful crystal pocket-sized angel. And said I must always keep it with me as a token of her love for me; and I have it in my purse right now. The nuns hugged me very warmly and I hugged them back and I smiled, and that was the first time I smiled that day.

Their coming made my day.

The ceremony and the reception were events that lasted a full day—a day that pleased my parents and my society; a full day that was the beginning of the life sentence I was to serve. Everyone was celebrating and in my deep sorrow I had to learn to smile and put my true feelings to hide in my 'turtle's shell.' No one ever asked me what I wanted, and again, I had no voice so I had to go along with the sentence—I could not defend myself.

In the eyes of our society, getting married was the decent and right thing to do. Now I was condemned to live a life I never wanted in situations I did not consent for. You see, I was dealing with the shame and disappointment I caused my parents, so this was, in a way, the right thing to do. But I felt like a criminal having decisions made for me like I was not there. I had no alternative to this predicament. I had one passion, and this was not it. Most people at least like each other and then get married. I did not like the man to whom I was now married. As a matter of fact, I was wrathfully angry with him.

After the grand day of the wedding, we went away for a 'honeymoon.' We left the reception and went to a lovely resort by the ocean about an hour from the city. We got into the car and not a word was said. As we got there, I told him we needed two rooms and those were the first words I said to him after exchanging vows. Hours prior, I said 'I do' to this man, but that was a lie I had to tell to please the masses of my community. He arranged the two rooms because there was no way I could stay in the same room with him.

I entered my room and stayed there in a daze, lost and in disbelief. We were there for seven days; I would go to the beach and walk for long distances and think about why I was there and what was ahead of me—I was petrified but had to come up with some different coping skills, going into my 'turtle's shell' was good but I needed a bit more now.

I was now smiling instead of crying—I was suppressing the pain and burying the truth. I felt I was having an out-of-body experience from the night of the convent up to now and I cannot wake up from this dream.

It was becoming easier and easier for me to act as I was expected to. There was a serious disconnect in my life. The reality of my life consumed me, but I had to deal with what was expected of me at the moment, it was always putting my true feelings aside, burying them.

When we were leaving to go to our flat to start our lives together, I was encouraged to say something to him, I said, "The life we had in the hotel was an example of the life we will live from this day on. You will have your space and I will have mine . . ."

One week later, the wedding was over, and my parents and my society were happy, and I was as sad as I could be. Getting ready to move to a different level of punishment, I left a comfortable hotel room to start living in the same space with my opponent. I said to him, "You and I know the truth of what this is—you had many opportunities to come forward and clear up this situation, but you did not. So, I will do what I must do until I can do what I want to do. Do not cross my path and I will not cross yours. I will show respect in the public's eye but out of the public's eye let there be nothing said or done that is not of my liking—and my liking is for us to be separate on this journey." I spoke to him only when it was necessary. After we moved into our flat, I told him which area I would occupy, and he must not come to that area under any condition.

I was forced to ripen into an adult with lots of responsibilities in an instant. I was sixteen years old with a husband and a child. This was not very uncommon in my society at that point in history. However, in most cases, it is where the two young people cannot stay away from each other, so it is a very acceptable thing for them to get married.

My husband was older and had completed his university studies and had a very good job. He provided well for me and the baby. He had ambitions to start his own business; and he did, he invested in precious jewelry and was successful at it. That added to the comfortable material life I shared with him; I did not have to work outside the home. I was a stay-at-home mom, and I did what was expected of me to maintain a life of respect and to regain the confidence of my parents and my society. I did not want to pay any more attention to my life.

My husband had a lot of insecurities about me, and he had every reason to because I never related to him since that horrible night when I was late getting back to the convent. Which I will disclose later.

I did not want him getting close to me, so I always kept a distance from him and stayed in the area I assigned for myself—sort of protected from him. I would lock my bedroom door each night and I kept an iron bar behind the door, just in case. I resented him. I could not make the horrible mistake of being pregnant again even if the situation were conducive to that—so I kept him at a distance always. I knew I never wanted another child. I would rather die.

I was filled with anger, disgust, resentment, and disappointment; because instead of living the life I wanted, I was burdened down with a life I did not consent to with a man I did not care about or respect. It was a life that was forced on me.

My life now is about marriage and raising my child. And all the things that went along with family life, all the things I never wanted. I learned how to hide my emotions very well and not show or expose to anyone how I really felt about anything. I was constantly in my 'turtle's shell.' Living the false pretense my life was built on, I would show up at some of the social events with my husband and would mingle with his friends and associates. But out of that limelight, I stayed in my own world. I had initially learned some coping skills from dealing with my father's alcoholism. Those skills helped me to do what was expected of me without issue and to avoid conflict by keeping my opinions and feelings to myself. At times, I had a lot of rage for my husband; and for my father as well for the emotional neglect he imposed on me. Nonetheless, I was coping with life the best way I knew how.

A year into the marriage my husband purchased a simple home that was appropriate for us in a different town from where I had grown up; I liked being away from my old area and the stigma that hung over me.

In the new home I tried to find peace in the life I was now living by taking care of my child, and creating a beautiful garden, which provided an escape from reality when I did not go into my 'turtle's shell.' In my garden, I found some inner joy, quietness, and peace.

When I sat in my garden the flowers turned toward me; the leaves danced for me; and the wind made music as it caressed the leaves. I had learned a lot about gardening during my pregnancy when I went into seclusion in my parents' orchard; and in my earlier years from my grandmother's friend whom I had shadowed.

In raising my child, I did my best and I learned through trial and error and asking questions when I was not sure what to do. My mother was always a good support. I raised my child and lived 'like a wife' in the eyes of the world but I was living in a prison without bars serving a life sentence for a crime I did not commit.

A few years went by, I was now about nineteen years old and the dream in me to serve God was still alive, I was still drawn to my spiritual life and service. I found a church I liked and attended regularly by myself and volunteered some of my time. My husband and I never worshipped together, he never went to church except for the day we got married. I spent a lot of time reading in my spare time, trying to gain a bit of what was taken from me earlier. I enrolled in classes and got private tutoring. Whenever there was some event that I needed to attend, I would, and I did it with grace. No one could guess what our life was like, and that is how I wanted it. My husband had many affairs, but I was not interested in that; I did not care.

A few years into the marriage, I wondered about my future and asked myself questions like: "Will my whole life exist just to live this false life and raise my child? Will it be without the education I wanted? I know I cannot be a nun anymore, and that killed me a little each day. What will happen when my child grows up and moves on, what purpose will I have with this man? How can I be happy burying my dream and trying to live as someone else's convenience?" Remember, I was an individual who had a specific dream. "What would happen if he eventually left, would he be dutiful toward me the rest of his life; was he sorry for what he did and this was his way of saying so; what if one of his affairs grew into more than just an affair, where would I be, how would I take care of myself and my child? Though my dreams were never for riches, they were for service in a certain way to humanity. But, without an education and not being supported by a convent, what kind of service would I be able to provide in exchange for a salary to take care of myself?"

I wanted to make choices for myself, and not have life and others make choices for me. I existed in a world with many but always felt extremely lonely. No one understood that this was not what I wanted and that my soul was drying up. Until one day I went for a walk in my neighborhood, a walk that would give some moisture to my soul.

Meeting My Soulmate

A few blocks away from my home, less than half a mile or so, some beautiful homes were being built. This was a new development with some pre-built homes and some custom-

designed homes mixed. I was amazed at how far along they had gone, and it was not long since they had started. I knew the houses were being built, and I had promised to go see what they looked like, and I was pleased. Looking at the construction, one home caught my interest, it was one of the custom designs. I felt connected to this house, a one-level ranch style home. I liked the side of the street it was on, the private balcony, the gardens that were now being designed and installed, and *the sturdy harbors where beautiful rose bushes could grow and fill in. I felt it was sort of a haven from all that was in my life. For a moment, I imagined myself living in that house, what a wish and a desire. I was daydreaming about the happiness I never had and was literally hoping the people for whom this home was being built would be happy. I was a sad person.*

I had no one to talk to about my deep fears, concerns, challenges, and regrets. Everything looked so right in my life—yet everything was so wrong. I stood in my daydream, imagining how to design the garden for this lovely home, a garden that would welcome the homeowners and nourish their souls, and in that thought, I lost track of time until the rain came. I had nowhere to go but under a partially finished roof at the side of the house, which looked like it would be part of a greenhouse area. I stood there hoping the rain would be a quick shower so I could return home. While sheltering and wishing the rain to stop, I was startled by what I had never seen or felt in my life.

I was startled by the 'hello' of a mild yet masculine voice which came from a gentleman who had an aura that captivated me. He was tall and pleasant to look at, ruggedly handsome, a football, athletic-sized guy, with broad strong shoulders. He said, "Hello." And I said, "I did not know anyone was here." After feeling awkward for what seemed like an entire day while gazing at him, I stretched out my hand and introduced myself. He smiled and said, "I was working out some figures after the workmen left so there was no noise. I am Zander, call me Zan." We stood there and looked at each other as if we had known each other for centuries. We said nothing. I felt I was seeing into his soul, and I thought he saw into mine. The rain was easing up, so I thanked him for the shelter and started to make my way off his property. As I walked home, there were some soft sprinkles that kept coming down and I loved that because they were moistening the dried-out parts of my soul, those parts that no one could see. I wondered who this person was, and what was that aura around him. I went home and could not get his image out of my mind. He consumed my thoughts. I spent all my awakening time for the next few days consumed with thoughts of him. I had many questions and no answers.

My marriage was one of convenience; it should not have been a marriage at all. It was one of my duties and responsibilities to please my community and my parents, but nonetheless, I was married. So, this thinking about another man was wrong in the eyes of my society, but not in my eyes.

A few days later, on a splendid day, I was working in my garden, it was after lunch, the time of day I love being outside, we only had one season on the island – hot. It may be raining, or it is dry, but it is always hot. This day was hot, dry, and quiet, and the beautiful ocean breeze kept things comfortable. Perfect time for a cat nap, or just sit and think, sometimes I would read. I loved how I felt at that time of the day. I was able to do all the other things I had to because of this garden—it was therapeutic and rewarding to me. In a way, it was like being on the lawns of the convent with gardens that existed for lifetimes; with beautiful unexplainable nooks and open places for all who are worthy of that life to enjoy. What I had created was a sanctuary where I came to be at peace and commune with nature and my flowers. I spent a lot of time in my sanctuary thinking about life and all the things I needed to do, and now I was thinking about Zan. At times I found myself talking out loud to him which is dangerous because I recently learned that Zan and my husband are business acquaintances.

As I tended my garden and took a breath to sit in my favorite place under the harbor of running pink roses; a spot from where I can see the front gate, I saw a car pull up, and out came this perfect specimen of a man, and before my eyes, it was Zan. He came to the gate and entered very comfortably since some people seemed to be stuck at the gate and not sure where to find the latch to unlock it. Zan said, "Hello, how are you? You look so peaceful sitting there." I told him to come in, as my garden was fenced in with a very nice white picket fence and gate. I told him I loved this spot. It is my favorite. It was where I saw the beauty of most of the garden. He came in, and I offered him a glass of lemonade. He said he was fine and just wanted to stop by and say 'hello.' We spoke for a few moments then he said he had to check on some building materials at the site of his home. He said, "After you left the other night, it came to my memory who you were, and I couldn't stop thinking of the interaction we had, and I was pulled to stop by to see if I could get another glimpse of you."

I smiled while he spoke and I looked at him, and there was that something in his eyes that captivated me even more. I could not explain what it was, but I knew I wanted to see it again. What was in his eyes? Was it for me, or was it just the way his eyes looked? As he left, I had a lot of stirred-up feelings and more questions. These were feelings of being attracted to someone and wanting to be with them, feelings I never had for another person.

Zan stopped by to see me on a few more occasions while I was in my garden, and we connected in a very lovely way each time.

A few months later Zan attended a social event where I

accompanied my husband—Zan was sitting at our table. After all, he is a business acquaintance of my husband, but his presence was tormenting me.

There was something electrifying about Zan–he raised my life's vibration to something I had not feel since being a child and wanting to be a nun.

I was now about twenty-one years of age and had come into myself—at that time in history in the Caribbean, twenty-one was the official age of being an adult. This is the age you can vote and do things without the consent or approval of a senior, or your parents. Now I can make my own decisions as I am no longer under anyone's jurisdiction.

At this gathering, Zan was unaccompanied, and I could feel the piercing of his eyes on me when I was not looking at him or in his direction. I was hoping no one could see his fixed eyes on me. He had no one to focus on so he was constantly looking in my direction. I desperately wished my husband would disappear as he had at many functions before; he would leave to be with one of his female companions for long moments but, I never paid any attention to him because I did not care. But that night, I wanted him to really disappear, but he did not.

I looked at Zan to signal to him I was getting up from the table; I left and walked about three or four tables away towards the bar area. As I looked around, Zan unsuspectingly was behind me, he left the table with everyone sitting there. We got close to each other where we felt safe, and just being in each other's presence filled us both for a moment. All I needed was a moment. Also, I wanted to look into his eyes without others looking at us, and our short intervals away from the social table allowed that. But regardless of how much I looked into his eyes, I wanted to see more because I could not understand what I was seeing and why I was thirsting for more.

That night, as the evening got older, Zan announced he was leaving for the evening, and we all wished him a good night. As he left the table and walked toward the exit, I felt a large part of me left with him. I felt empty and alone, yet I was there with my husband and many friends. I could not enjoy the evening anymore as Zan took the wind out of my sail when he left.

Private Meeting with my Soulmate

My husband was always on business trips for weeks at a time, and I think he included his female companions on many trips. This was good that he was constantly gone because I did not like having him around; and when he was around, he had his own area of the home, and I had mine, so our lives were separate. Nonetheless, he was getting ready for a trip and was scheduled to be leaving in a few days. By this time, a week or so had passed since I last saw Zan. I continued with my schedule, as there were lots to do with my lifestyle which I created for myself, taking care of my child, maintaining the home, and managing my garden and myself. Then he left for his trip.

I continued my normal schedule for a few days of my husband being gone, then one day out of nowhere, when I was not overwhelmed with thoughts of Zan, he showed up. I looked up, and there he was. He walked from his home to mine, and I was in my usual spot in my garden. He said he had some issues with his builder and decided to walk away from the situation to clear his head and ended up at my garden gate. "Hello there, Rose, how are you?" I was very happy to see him. I invited him in, and I sat in my favorite spot while he sat on a garden bench close by. I offered him a passion-fruit beverage, and he accepted. He stretched out his well-sculpted body on the bench and looked at me and said, "You are a very special woman." I asked him why he said that, and he said, "Because you are. And there is something about you that is intriguing. You never seem to let anyone know what you are thinking, and there is something in your eyes." Then he stayed quiet and looked at me. Our eyes met and locked for what seemed like the rest of the afternoon. What I saw again was a look that said all I never saw in any pair of eyes that ever looked at me.

After a few moments, he stood up and placed his hands on mine. I felt the earth move, as he towered over me, I felt safe in this intimate space with him. I did not move my hand because I liked the sensation I was experiencing. My vibration was rising to such a high pitch... At that moment, I realized this was something real. This is that once-in-a-lifetime situation that people dream about and wish for; passionate love from the heart with strong physical attraction, this I had heard and read about and seen in the movies, but never wanted or expected for myself. I then placed my other hand on top of his. It was a gesture that said, yes, I want this! He asked, "Is it possible for us to have some sips and chips elsewhere sometime?" And I said, "Of course, I will let you know when I have some free time, I will call you."

As he left, I kept thinking of what had just happened. Zan touched my hand . . . You see, I was never touched or hugged by my dad. And my marriage did not consist of those ingredients. I never knew what it was for a man to touch me with love and tenderness, and I never felt I wanted that until I met Zan, and now that he touched me...

With my husband being away, it was the perfect time for me to go out without explaining my whereabouts, or the possibility of him seeing me somewhere dining with anyone.

Two days later, after calming myself down, I called Zan to schedule a time for us to meet. We met at 6:00 pm., two afternoons later at a restaurant on the oceanfront with seats overlooking the ocean; we had dinner and spoke for a while and ended the evening at a decent hour with a plan to see each other in a more private setting next time. He shared his concerns about me being in public with him and I was concerned too as I did not want or need another scandal or disgraceful situation in my life. I was elated spending time with him and could not wait to be with him again.

A few days later, we met at a private hotel suite early in the evening. I arranged things at home so I did not have to be available to anyone until the next day because I knew I would have an experience that would be out of this world. And did not want anything interrupting my thoughts or feelings, I needed a spot of time for me.

We entered the private hotel suite, where there were finger food and drinks already set up. We sat and got comfortable. I laid my hand in his, and the energy that flowed between us was more than speaking to each other. The vibrational of our energies could light up the entire island...We sat there for a moment in silence. I knew that there was nothing to fight about, nothing to fear, and nothing to worry about. I knew that this man was not there to force himself on me even though the setting was conducive to that. He adjusted his position so he could look me in the eyes, and then he said just what I was thinking. He said, "Rose, I am not here to have sex with you, I am here to get to know you." And at that moment he confessed something to me that blew me away. He said, "I have known you for a long time. I knew when you went away to the convent through a friend who lived on your street who always had wonderful things to say about you. I know what happened to you. And I have loved you since then. It was hard not knowing about your situation when it happened—it was often spoken of, and a lot of people felt your pain—I was one of those people. Also, the day I saw you at the construction of my home, I was in shock and could not believe it was you for I had not seen you or any pictures of you in a while and you have matured into a very beautiful woman. You really are beautiful. I would love to have you as my own. But I know that is selfish." I was shocked! He continued saying, "What I want is different. I want to love you, and whatever comes with that is fine. Sex gets in the way, and I take this as an opportunity to be in your life in a special way. I want to be someone you can trust, I want to be that someone in your corner, if you would let me. And before we go any further, I want you to know I respect the chance you have taken to be here with me. I wished for the opportunity to meet you one day, and that happened miraculously and had me in shock – questioning if it was really you.

Through the years, I always found out about you indirectly. I could not imagine what you had gone through and how you lived through all that. Your story caused me to care for you in a deep way from afar. I know we are not supposed to be together, but I will stand by you in anything that ever happens to you and to us. I am prepared to do what is needed for you today and for the rest of my life. The only thing that will stop me from standing at your side is death. I want to spend special quality time with you, and that cannot happen in public as you are still married. I know this is wrong in the eyes of society, but I have never felt so sure about anything in my life. I want to be in your corner, I want to be in your life, I would accept just friendship if that were all you are prepared to give."

What Zan did in those few moments was exceptional. In my mind, this was the next best thing to being a nun. To be with a man I gravitated toward—handsome, humble, ambitious, and powerful with a gentle soul.

Disbelief consumed me for a few moments because I wanted the friendship he offered. Somehow, I knew he would not be about sex; I saw more in his soul. I have looked into my husband's eyes, and I do not think he has a soul; he is just a physical being looking for physical pleasures, where and how he can get them. This experience with Zan was mind-blowing the way he stated his position. I thought he would look for the benefit of sexual pleasure, but what he said to me was an explanation of what I saw in his eyes the first time I saw him, and every time since. That is what I wanted to see again and again. And when I understood what it was, I still wanted more. It was gentle, genuine, and caring. He looked at me as if he were looking at a queen or a beautiful baby—with warm eyes. I love the reflection of me I saw in him.

Once my mind was stretched to the experience of Zan, it was difficult for me to regain peace in my life as it were. What I knew for sure at that point was I did not want a loveless marriage anymore; a life of pretense, showing the world we were a family and living in hell behind the walls of the house we lived in. I loved everything about Zan, I loved the way he smelled, the way he looked at me, the way I felt in his presence, in his arms, his voice, and his way of thinking. I loved his soul. I could never get enough of him. I always felt sad when we parted, and when we hung up the phone. I felt complete with him. Something about me never cared about sex, but I cared deeply about nourishing my soul with Zan's love and the tenderness that came from him.

I felt I was tarnishing myself by being in the marriage, sharing the same home and name of a man I had no feelings for, except contempt. The situation became very difficult. What I felt about Zan was exceptional. I felt the need to be available to him whenever he needed me. Months into the relationship, meeting when and where we could, talking every day, and no sexual intimacy; yet I felt so intimate with him that sex did not matter. Or did it?

When I was in my home and doing anything in the life I had, I felt I was being unfaithful to Zan. And I thought I should try to forget him and continue with what I had, but that was impossible. The more I tried to deny my feelings for Zan, the stronger they grew. My daily chores and showing up with my husband at social events were killing me unless Zan was there, and I could see him. Why can't I be with Zan? Why can't I be happy? I love Zan, why did I have to be with this man I was married to?

Zan's home was close to completion, and I was taking more frequent walks in the neighborhood. My walks were the highlight of many of my days and a favorite past time of mine when my husband was away. At least I knew that no one would be looking for me and that gave me a sense of freedom to go visit Zan. I would come back from my visits and sit in my garden at night and savor the excitement and the energy of being with him.

Then, one evening, I went for my usual walk to see him and to give him some ideas about decorating and some color selections; we walked around the house and looked at the different rooms, stopping and discussing paint colors and furnishings and ended up in his bedroom, mainly because it was the only furnished room in the house. I sat on his bed, and he came and sat next to me. I felt a strong energy flowing between us, my vibration raised…and I knew that night I needed to tell Zan something he did not know. I started shaking as he got close to me, and he wanted to know what was happening. He said, "Do not ever be uncomfortable with me. I will never hurt you." I got closer to him and said, "Zan, there is something I need to tell you." He said, "Please tell me." I said, "Zan, I have never made love, I have never had sex."

Zan stood up and held his head and said, "Could you repeat that?" I said, "I have never been sexually intimate with anyone. I never had sexual intercourse.

Please sit, Zan. I must tell you this. My husband, when he was a new friend in my life and I was in the convent, one night on my way back from the weekend off, he offered to escort me after we had been hanging around with a few other friends. We did this a few times, and on that trip back we stopped for some soda pop and went along a different route that was supposed to be a shortcut, one we had not taken before. There was always a group of us going all the way to the convent or very close to it. But that afternoon it ended up with just the two of us as everyone had gone their separate ways. Before I knew it, we were off the beaten path. There was a lot of activity along this path: people were walking their dogs, some parents and children taking walks, and seniors just strolling. I never felt I was in any danger. Then in a moment, realizing we were at a quiet spot, he started pulling me close to him, trying to kiss and hold me tight. And I guess never being hugged, a part of me may have allowed it, and before long, he took advantage of me as I had passed out from such an overwhelming experience.

Moments later I found myself laying on the ground—pulled into the bushes—with him shaking me, apologizing profusely, and crying.

All the scandal and leaving the convent stemmed from that, and after the baby was born, he was pressured into marrying me by the community and my parents. I have held him in contempt since that night and have never allowed him to touch me since then. I have never revealed this to anyone until now. We just live in the same house, and we are married, but we never consummated the marriage, and we never will—I will not let it.

My parents and the community thought I had consensual sex with him.

Zan fell on his knees before me and dropped his head in my lap. He was silent, and then he said, "Of all the things I have heard, this is by far the most shocking. Rose, I am so sorry this is what you suffered. I knew you had a level of sadness in you, but how did you deal with such pain on your own? Please know from this moment forward, you never have to suffer alone." He held me and would not let me go, and his hugs got tighter and tighter as if he wanted me to become a part of him. I asked him, "Would you make love to me?" He did not answer, and for a moment I wondered if he would, because of the stigma I just explained to him.

He placed two of his fingers on my lips in the gesture for me to be quiet, and he started kissing me, which went from the top of my head to the bottom of my feet. Gentle kisses as if he were trying to erase all the pain I suffered and I felt like a woman for the first time and wondered if this is what all couples did. I never wanted this sort of thing, I wanted a different life, but with Zan, I felt so right, so perfect, so loved, so safe.

I gave myself to Zan that night, body, mind, and soul.

A few hours later Zan said, "I am honored. And I will never hurt you. I will stand by you always, and whatever you want to do I will support you; I do not want to impose anything on you to cause you further pain, just know whatever you want from me, or of me—it is yours."

When Zan and I came together that night, we became one. In the marriage vows it says—and the two shall become one—that is what happened with Zan and me. I felt the world stopped at that moment so we could intertwine and become one. Our souls were consummated. I could never call the man I was married to my husband again, not after that night—I mentally divorced him. He was the man I was married to, not my husband. All the hugs and love I never got from my father, and the hurt I experienced with the man to whom I am married—Zan compensated for that night. After the love I have for God, this is my second love, and nothing can penetrate this.

Zan refused to let me walk home alone that night, as it

was now late, so he walked with me. On the walk home, it took all the restraint in me not to hold his hand or put my arms around his waist. As we walked along, he reminded me that he would never leave me and that he would take care of me; and he would be my friend and confidant and could offer me a different life, a life of love. He said he would need two lifetimes to show me the love he had for me. While I enjoyed what Zan offered, I could not imagine the second round of disgrace this would cause if I left the man I was married to, or if this affair got exposed. I told him we must be careful until we figure out how to handle this situation.

With our affair at another level, it brought on new issues for me. I wanted to continue my life as the other part of Zan. I wanted to have a life of serving God and then being a helpmate to Zan—however that could be combined. I did not get to be a nun, maybe I could get Zan as my second choice, but he was forbidden, because I was married.

Months went by, and we saw each other as often as possible. We spoke every day. Zan became a drug for me; I could not get enough of him. For the first time since my childhood, I am feeling loved and finding joy in life. With all this, everything changed with the way I looked, I was glowing, and life had meaning. Nonetheless, I had to get away from what was consuming me and from what had me entrapped. Because every time I spent time with Zan, it was difficult to come back to a life with no meaning and be using the name of a man I could not stand.

I had more questions than answers for my life now. The affair was causing me to avoid other parts of my life. I could not go on this way; I was at a crossroads and did not know what to do. I must get out of this situation, but which one? Should I go with Zan and leave the 'sort of secure' life I was settled into; or should I leave Zan and go back to what I had before? The latter was impossible.

It was about eighteen months into my affair and my turmoil was beyond me. I could not go to church because I did not know what to pray for; I was living a life of sinfulness—the more I saw Zan—the more I did not want the life I had; and the more I realized I could not have Zan without serious complications. I tried not to see Zan for a few weeks; he reluctantly accepted that idea, and it was too much for me to deal with, and I started feeling very ill. I was emotionally ill, I had severe physical results. It reminded me of the signs of pregnancy, but I was not pregnant. I took every necessary precaution and Zan was very careful not to let that happen to me, and it did not. The man I was married to arranged for me to see one doctor after another, and no one could find what was wrong with me (I knew what was wrong with me). I was told to take some time off from my daily routine, I tried to relax and occupy myself with different activities, but nothing worked. I wanted Zan, I needed Zan. Just to see him, be around him, talk to him, listen to him, his jokes, his plans for life, his philosophy, I wanted to smell and hug him. You see, I was ill because my life's vibration was very low without him.

Escaping from Emotional Turmoil

After a lot of contemplation and deep thought, I realized I could not go on like this. I could not live with what I had, and I could not accept what was being offered by Zan. I decided I would leave the life I had, leaving everything behind in search of my truth. But how? The planning and thinking of getting all this done overwhelmed me and made me more ill. I was able to convince the man I was married to that I would go to a neighboring island to visit a friend I had and relax for a few weeks. He immediately agreed and started planning the trip for me. However, unknown to him, I contacted another friend who lived on another island further away letting her know I would be coming to visit her in a couple of weeks and for her to keep this a secret until I got there.

I contacted Zan who was happy to hear from me but in his own turmoil about this affair, I asked him for us to meet at a private setting—not his home. I told him we must meet. I have made a decision...

The evening was perfect, the man I was married to was out of town. I took another opportunity to meet Zan at a hotel suite, the same one we met the first time. He arranged for finger foods and a few beverages. This time when we got behind closed doors, he told me all the things I needed to hear. And how much he loved and cared for me and that he wanted a life with me; we looked at each other, and then we sat and got comfortable. I still looked into his soul, that look was there like the first time I saw him. I started crying, and he cried too. He said just what I was thinking. He said, "You have something very difficult to tell me," And I said, "yes, I do."

I said, "Zan, I cannot continue with what we have. It is too difficult for me; I need to go away for a while to clear my head and think about what I need to do with my life." He said he knew it was very hard for me. We did not talk much, we spent most of the time in silence just holding each other. We ended the evening as we started our first one over eighteen months ago, we did not make love. We held each other and confessed our love. After that night it was a few weeks before I called him. I tried to break the bond and clear my head by not calling and refusing his calls, but I missed him so much I got gravely ill and was dropping weight rapidly. Everyone was concerned about me and had suggestions for different doctors I should see. Politely I accepted their offers and went about my life because I knew what was wrong with me and I was choosing to fix it—hopefully.

I went on my short trip with the assistance of the man I was married to, and I arranged things for my child to have the proper care and coverage on everything I could think of. As I left, I knew in my heart I would not be coming back to this life—I was leaving it for good. I asked my mom to step in on my behalf and do what was necessary for my child. With my mom, the man I was married to, and the help we had who assisted in the home, my child would be fine for a bit. And with just a carry-on bag and my purse, I said good-bye to my mom, kissed my child, and left. I left for a two-week vacation—but I had other plans that would keep me going on to an unknown life many islands or maybe countries away—I was willing to take this chance. I had to save myself and this was the only possible way. I had to make my own choices even if I ended up on a rocky road or in a trash heap. I could not live this way anymore.

The man I was married to contacted me to be sure I was where I was supposed to be. I rested for about two to three days, just laying around in the hotel room and using room service. I went to two dinners with my friend who insisted that I stay at her home, but I graciously refused because that would contaminate my continuing plans. Then I contacted my friend who was much further away (countries away) and started making plans to visit her, which I knew was the real trip to the destination I was going to live out my life making choices for myself.

Deep down I looked forward to life away from the convent that did not happen, away from the peering eyes of my community, the marriage that was not a marriage, and the inability to be with the love of my life.

I would make something of myself, I will go back to school and gain that education I was deprived of that I wanted so desperately, and I would be the woman I was created to be. So, help me God!

The time away gave me the opportunity to analyze my affair—I hungered for Zan. I called to let him know I was off the island and did not have a chance to say goodbye when I was leaving. He said he understood and would love to come and be with me; I was tempted by the offer but refused. Zan and I spoke for about two nights, only stopping in between for food and bathroom breaks. He was willing to follow me and for us to have a life together. Every scenario he presented was tempting, but finally I said, "no." I said 'no' to the additional shame and disgrace, not just for me, but for him. I did not want him to be faced with this all his life. He shared many of his life plans with me and this would be a big disruption for him. So, sadly, and unselfishly, I declined and hung up the phone, it was seven years before I spoke to Zan again.

I had less than two weeks to plan the second leg of my trip and enough money for about six months of living expenses and a few pieces of jewelry I could sell. It was very difficult to leave without telling my friend thanks for her hospitality, but I had to make an escape and move on to my next destination, and that took a lot of thinking and coordination. I eventually got things together and left two days before I was scheduled to go back home. This was an uncomfortable move for me, and I was looking over my shoulder constantly. I felt that Zan would show up, and I also thought that the man I was married to would show up. I was very uncomfortable. But luckily, no one showed up, at least I did not see anyone.

The next leg of my journey was hours of flying. I was weak and mentally exhausted, but I did not exhale until the plane doors closed. All the way to the airport, and while at the airport, I was close to fainting because I felt someone would show up and stop my plan and get in my way. The plane was sitting on the tarmac for a long time waiting to take off, and I was uncomfortable because of all that I was dealing with. I was praying that all was well, and we would not be taken off the plane and sent back to the airport. I was scared. I was on the run. I felt like a fugitive. I was running from life and at the same time running to life.

The plane finally took off, and I was on my way. The stress of all I had gone through over the last few months had weakened me, and I was nauseated on the flight for a while. And after what seemed like an infinity, I arrived at my destination—London.

Starting Life Elsewhere

I arrived in London physically ill, confused about the time difference and consumed with jet lag and weak knees. Everything was supposed to be beautiful according to what my friend had shared with me, and all I saw in pictures through the years. But on my arrival and in the taxicab to my friend's flat everything was a blur. I felt close to death's door, but I kept breathing.

I was happy to see my friend waiting to welcome me, but I was too sick to think or do anything, I needed to rest, and nothing stayed in my stomach. My friend insisted I see a doctor, but I knew I needed to rest and get my mind calm, and I did not need a doctor to tell me that. I sat up after about five days and was beginning to understand what time of the day it was, my body's clock was starting to adjust. I woke up to reality and to a whole new set of issues.

How am I going to exist in this situation? Immediately, I knew I would not fit into the circle my friend associated with. It was all about the designer dresses, the parties, the pocketbooks, and all the things I had no interest in. I was always a very simple person and I saw myself in my nun's habit day in and day out and never felt I would ever get tired of that, so designer labels and all that stuff were of no importance to me. Nonetheless, I did not go there to live the life my friend was living, I went there as a place to take shelter while I moved on and get my feet on the ground, make my own decisions, and carve out a life for myself.

A few weeks went by in this situation, I could not get better because of what was ahead. All my fears looked me in the face. I did not have an education nor the proper papers to live and work on this island. I could live as a Caribbean citizen as London is our mother country, but I could not work without a work permit, which made it difficult.

Applying for a work permit meant I would have to give acceptable reasons and references of why I wanted to work there; and as a married woman, my husband must approve.

I had about six months' worth of money to get by on, so things did not look hopeful. I knew I would face these realities but when I was making my plans my focus was to get away from the life I had; and now, I was faced with new issues that I was not sure how to approach.

I knew I could not stay with my friend indefinitely and I was paying my way to stay with her. There was nowhere else for me to go. Stepping out of my friend's home would mean going to a homeless shelter. But really, I was homeless. My friend knew I had a comfortable existence with the man I was married to, and she saw me as an opportunity to get some of her bills paid down. She was taking lots of money from me and had inflated the price for her rent and utilities, and with me not knowing any better, I would give her lots of money to stay in her flat. I was paying more than half of all her bills and sleeping on her floor. Nonetheless, I was thankful for shelter and not to be in the streets.

My friend had a boyfriend who visited regularly, and whenever he came by, I would go for a walk in the neighborhood and sit in a park I found a few blocks away and read my Bible. I did not want my friend to feel she lost her privacy by having me there. This boyfriend was a good dresser and spent lots of money on clothes. My friend would tell me about the costs of his shirts and shoes; he wore only the best, and he was also a womanizer.

One day while I was at home alone and my girlfriend was at work, he came by with the intention of forcing himself on me. He saw me as another woman he wanted to have an experience with but had no idea of the struggles I had gone through. I knew this was not going to happen to me again. So, when he approached and attacked me, I defended myself. I was not the little girl who knew nothing of life. I had suffered and was in a compromising situation because of what a man did to me, at the age of fourteen, when I was totally innocent. I was not about to suffer any other consequence for any similar situation. This was not going to happen. So, as he approached me, in that moment of anger, disgust, frustration, lost dreams, disgrace, and advantage taken on me; I grabbed a vase that was sitting on the coffee table and hit him in the face with all the strength I had. I weighed about 110 pounds, but the force that came behind that vase was probably more than 300 pounds; it was the years of pain I suffered, the way my life is now, and the prevention of further pain.

I injured him badly, and if he had not run out of that flat, in that instance, who knows what else could have happened to him? There was blood everywhere, but I kept my dignity. And that is all that matters to me. No one was going to violate me, no one. Not again!

His injuries had to be hospital-treated; he ended up with many stitches to hold his face together. He failed in his attempt to seduce me. Now I was scared that my friend would ask me to leave, and I knew no one else, and I had nowhere to go. But I knew that I would take my chances and let my friend know exactly what happened, and I did. My friend was upset at her boyfriend and knew that he had no reason to be visiting the flat at a time when she was at work. His timing was the evidence that my girlfriend held against him. Also, she knew I was not looking for anything like that in my life; I had enough challenges of my own.

Shortly thereafter, that additional stress caused my face and body to break out into bumps that turned into blisters. There was no clear skin on any part of me. I looked scornful. But I needed a job and a place of my own, and my money was running low. What I average would last for six months was almost finished.

Four months had passed, and my face was beginning to clear up a bit; and I invested in some cheap make-up to cover my scarred face to look a bit presentable. Without the proper clothes, education, and work permit, I had to look for jobs that did not require much skill, and no proof of paperwork. I had nothing. I was looking for day jobs to clean homes or wash and iron clothes where people would pay as you completed the work. Those jobs did not need any documentation. I got a few jobs here and there and was humiliated by each one. People would hire you to clean the filthiest parts of their homes for the lowest pay imaginable. But there again, I had no choice.

During this time, I was encouraged to contact a distant friend of my friend who knew people who might be able to assist in some way with the type of jobs I was doing. I called and introduced myself to see where that would lead, she was willing to assist but said it would be difficult without the right papers. Nonetheless, she called a few days later with a lead on a job that did not need all the paperwork and red tape. It was for a few days a week, accompanying a senior citizen to her doctor's appointments, cleaning her home, cleaning up her personal mess because she had many accidents as she was getting down in age, cooking for her, and making sure she took her medication. I was humiliated doing these jobs but had no other choice at the time. I accepted my new reality and was excited for the lead.

While doing this job a few days a week, one day on a bus I saw a small crowd of women standing on a corner close to a hardware store and overheard two women on the bus talking about the crowd of women. They were saying those women would gather there and wait for people to come pick them up for day jobs. They were female day workers; and across the street were the male day laborers. People who needed day workers would pick these people up and when the job was finished, they brought them back to the same spot. Before long, on the days I had no work—I joined the crowd of women and got some work. I was treated like the scum of the earth. I was scared at times for my safety but was never hurt physically in any way. I felt the presence of my angels around me.

I cried each time I cleaned a bathroom, and if people were around and asked if I was okay—I would say chemicals got into my eyes. I cried whenever I got lost trying to find a job or was treated badly; I cried because I had no other way to get by financially. My tears at this time did not always flow outward, and I found myself crying inwardly.

One day, I was asked if I could stay over the evenings and weekends to do a bit more with the senior that I was caring for. She told her family she liked the way I treated her with dignity and would like me around more. For me, it would be a bit more money and I thought it best for me to accept it, and I did. It also meant having a place to sleep on a sofa bed and not my friend's cold hard floor. After a few months, the senior's nephew, a barrister-at-law, came by and asked for my proper papers to claim income taxes on me. I was in jeopardy. But asked if I could bring my papers the next week when I went home. When I left that weekend with my few pieces of clothing in a plastic garbage bag, all old and worn out, I was at a low place spiritually. I never received that last paycheck which was for a few weeks. All the checks I had received thus far were compromised; since I did not have a bank account, I had to endorse my checks to my friend who would deposit them in her account and then give me the cash. And she always had money issues. I had one set of problems and she had another, hers were about all the bills she had. I felt guilty doing anything for myself, buying anything—it was impossible to buy as much as a new blouse for myself to go on an interview or a pair of slippers or shoes for my feet that were almost on the ground.

I contacted my mother on a few occasions to let her know I was okay and to find out how my precious child was doing. My mother was supportive and very sad about the life I was living. She would always tell me to take care of myself and to come home if it were too difficult, and that I would not have to go back to the life I had, it would be okay.

On one occasion when I called my mother, the man I was married to was visiting her and he came on the phone yelling and screaming at me saying, "YOU NEED TO COME HOME NOW! YOU WILL NEVER MAKE IT WITHOUT ME!"

I quietly said, "Never, will I come back to you, I would die first." And I hung up.

On the next call to my mom, she said he just took the phone from her the minute he realized I was on the phone without her being able to notify me. It was disgusting hearing his voice and I reminded myself there and then, I would never go home regardless of what happened to me. Going home meant he would have access to me, and I did not want to be dependent on my parents. I had to find another job, so I was on the hunt.

At this time of my journey, the bottom of my feet were on the ground; I was wearing the only pair of sandals I had that I brought with me from home. It was still warm in London so I was stuffing pieces of cardboard from the inner part of the toilet tissue wrapper and the paper towel holder in the sole of my sandals so my feet would not be on the pavement. I did a lot of walking and that was the only pair of footwear I had. I was so sure that with the money I left home with I would have been able to purchase a few new things for me to get by. Also, my sandals went along with the few pieces of clothing I had which were worn out now, just a step away from rags. I looked like a pauper, and not to mention some rashes still on my face.

In my mind, I knew that education was the only way out of this struggle, but I had no way of venturing into education at this time.

With money running desperately low I decided to sell a few pieces of jewelry. But never being exposed to anything like this, I was nervous. I did not want the jewelry store to think I stole the jewelry because I looked like I could never own any of the pieces I was trying to sell. I prayed not to be questioned because I had no receipts for these pieces, I spoke with a Caribbean accent, and I did not have any documentation to even identify myself as being a resident here. I was almost shaking and trying to cover it by looking elsewhere. The clerk took the pieces and came back shortly to inform me of their value; he told me they were worth a decent amount of money which was much more than I was expecting. The exact worth of the pieces was unknown to me, so I had to trust his word. I felt a bit of joy for a brief second—just a second. And I asked if I could get the funds in cash, or at least most of it. I was prepared to take a loss at whatever had to be given in a cheque because once my girlfriend saw what I had she would have a need for most of it. I wanted a larger amount in cash so I would not have to disclose to her exactly what I had. I stood there praying hard for God and my guardian angels to work out a miracle on my behalf because I did not want to get into any trouble with these pieces.

The clerk went to the back of the store and took a long time before returning to me; during that time, I was wondering if I should leave, I had no idea what to do. I did not want to leave my jewelry, so I kept waiting and hoping for the best. Finally, the clerk appeared and apologized for the delay. I think he saw I was in a dilemma and after saying they do not give cash in these amounts, he paused, and I was praying hard with my fingers crossed, please God, a small miracle, please. Then he said, "I will make an exception for you." I felt relieved—then he gave me the full equivalent in cash, every penny of it. I took my money and left the store after thanking him, and then silently thanked God and my angels. I wanted to get to a place where I could stand and brace myself and take a breath and that happened about two buildings away. After taking a few breaths and calming my nerves, I looked up and there was the brightest blue sky, and a shoe store across the street to the corner, and that is where I went next.

I immediately bought two pairs of footwear. One pair I instantly put one on my feet while I placed the ones I took off in the empty box and tossed them in the garbage bin on my way out. My feet felt supported by the thick soles of my new shoes, and my feet exhaled.

While in the shoe store, I saw some advertisements for jobs through agencies that employed people to assist the elderly in their daily lives. I decided to take some information and join an agency; there again, luckily, I met with a wonderful man who gravitated toward me. He was older, kind, and soft-spoken. I filled out the paperwork and told some untruths while asking God to forgive me in advance. This would not hurt anyone; I just need to work, that is all. Luck would have it that the agency needed someone to go on a job immediately to a client who requested someone to live on the premises with one weekend off a month. The client was an elderly woman of class and grace who lived in a prestigious area on the outskirts of London. I had no car and no idea where the area was, but I knew I was going there. I took the address and started on my venture.

I wanted to work, and I would like a bed or a sofa to sleep on in a safe environment and receive pay for my work, which was my goal.

Ms. Smith, the client, did not need a lot of personal assistance. She needed to have someone around and initially, she wanted someone older and had refused a few younger workers, but she connected to me immediately. The agency told her I was a very settled young lady that she would like. And she did.

It took me half a day to get to the assignment after putting the best of my rags in a bag and finding my way by bus. After a certain distance, the busses did not go into the secluded areas but luckily, I had a few dollars from the jewelry I had sold, so I took a taxi to Ms. Smith's home. The huge, gated home and the beautiful tree-lined streets reminded me of some of the homes in the vicinity of the convent and in some of the rich neighborhoods on my Island. The very tall iron fence around this home was intimidating and so was the gate to enter, and the house sat a good distance from the gate with a circular driveway. I could see that the homes where Zan had built copied some of the architectural designs of the homes here. I guess by now the trees on his street are stretching their limbs to reach the sky. I wonder how he is doing, one day I will have a lot of stories to tell him.

I rang the doorbell and after a few moments, Ms. Smith opened the 'strong heavy' door that was shining black, which looked hand polished, and designed with some metal trim. She greeted me, and said, "Thank you for coming my child— I need someone here with me." Ms. Smith and I connected instantly. She looked at me, and I smiled, I felt a warm genuine love coming from her, she took me around the first floor of her home and then to 'my room' which was on the second floor and told me to make myself comfortable and then come down to her. This was a room for a princess! I talked myself out of crying. Could I go from sleeping on my friend's floor to sleeping on this? I looked out the beautiful bay window decorated with crystals facing west and at that time of the afternoon, the sun was directly on those crystals sending rays of beautiful colors all over the room.

This room overlooked a large well-manicured lawn and garden with beautiful flowers. I could not believe this, and the pay for this job was excellent. I did not know what the correct salary was for such work, but I was very happy and thankful for this opportunity. For me, this was the opportunity of a lifetime, and I was thankful.

After spending the rest of the afternoon into the evening getting acquainted with my duties and the way Ms. Smith liked things done; I retired to my room and was uncomfortable sleeping in the bed with my rags so, I walked around the room examining all the nooks and crannies and found that to the end of the bedroom was a glass door, and in front of it hung lace curtains. I pulled the curtains, and there was a balcony that went from that room all along the back of the house. I opened the door and went out onto the balcony. It was unbelievable, a private balcony from my room for me to relax and enjoy the evenings. Thank you, God, is this for real? I appreciate this. I took my shawl, one of the best things I had, put it around my shoulders, and went out on the balcony with my Bible and spent a few hours there. As I came in from the balcony, I folded my shawl and placed it at the foot of the bed with my Bible and I laid on the floor, on my back, and looked at the ceiling until the sun came up.

The next day Ms. Smith gave me a full tour of the rest of her home, and a lovely one-bedroom flat to the side of her home with its own private entrance that she leased out to a young professional. The only connection is that they could access the backyard if they wanted to. This was a very beautiful home and Ms. Smith opened everything to me.

Ms. Smith and I got along extremely well. As if we had been together for a long time. I did what she asked to the best of my ability, and I did lots of extra work in her garden. She was the recipient of that extra work, but I enjoyed tending to the rose bushes and the flowers and being in my element, which was therapeutic for me.

With the urgency to fill the position, the agency did not check all the back-up documentation, and I was able to settle in and get a regular paycheck working for Ms. Smith.

After about a month, one day, I accompanied Ms. Smith to the bank and while there I asked if I could open an account, and on her behalf I did. I opened my own account and deposited my few weekly checks and was happy I did not have to do anything with my money other than save. I also deposited the cash I had for the jewelry I sold. I was elated for this step in my life.

One evening watching television, I saw an advertisement for a three-month computer and office technology course in the evenings. The location for this course was about a twenty-minute walk from Ms. Smith's home. I wanted to take this course but was uncomfortable being out at night alone. But it was early evening, and I felt the neighborhood was safe and I could take a chance so, I discussed it with Ms. Smith, and it was fine by her.

I went to my class and spent my evenings studying. Ms. Smith would wait until I came in before she retired for the evening, and I would clean up and do the dishes before venturing to my studies. I enjoyed learning something new and felt happy going to class and studying after I got back and finished with my chores.

While there with Ms. Smith, I never locked my bedroom door because I did not feel I had a right to do that, but I would pull it to a certain degree and leave it ajar. One night I was kneeling on the floor praying, and Ms. Smith was at the door peeking at me, I did not know until she walked off. The next day she asked if I would like to accompany her to church, and I was elated! I said, "I would love that immensely." From that week I went to church with Ms. Smith regularly and I lived at her home all the time. I did not take time off to visit my friend, but I called her weekly to say 'hello.'

Ms. Smith was a woman of absolute class. One day she mentioned she had some things she was donating to the church and other charities, and I was welcome to see if there was anything I was interested in. She saw the rags I was wearing and knew this was an indirect way to offer me some decent pieces of clothing. It was amazing what Ms. Smith was giving away. I took a few pieces, one of the pieces was a beautiful lace and cotton night dress and the others were appropriate for church and while accompanying her to appointments and going to my class. I did not need much. I loved that night dress so much that *I would hand wash it gently each morning and hang it in the bathroom so it could dry by the evening when I took my shower. After receiving that night dress, I was comfortable going to bed.*

In school I was struggling to understand new concepts being taught on the computer; as I am dyslexic, and my dyslexia could sometimes be challenging when learning new things, I was learning a lot of new things; understanding how to get around in a new city; learning the bus system and learning to be careful and not to be too trusting. I had been sheltered all my life until now. And even though I was not a nun, I was living like one. Many young men would try to talk to me, but I kept wearing my wedding band and would tell them I was married to keep them off. However, there was a young man in the class who showed me a lot of interest and would come by in a gentle manner and assist me through my struggles and that helped me tremendously. I thanked him and kept quiet as I did not want to bring any attention to myself.

Another day at school I had to go to a different class because the instructor for my class was not there. In that class, I met another young man who paid me more attention than was needed. When the class was over, he made his way to me and walked me out of the building and to the street. I was trying to get away from him but could not—so I made some excuses to go my way and promised to talk with him another time.

As I completed my chores and retired to my room as usual there was a beautiful 'pink and cream lace pattern' gift bag on my bed; my eyes were bouncing around like a pair of tennis balls on a court and I was wondering if I died and went to heaven; or was someone allowed in who was looking for me and this was a surprise, would someone jump out of the closet now? The only one I would want such a surprise from was my mom. I was waiting for something to happen, but nothing happened. I approached the bag and peeked at the beautiful matching tissue paper and saw a card that said (To Rose, I appreciate you—From Ms. Smith). It took me forever to look inside the bag because the card was so beautiful—that was enough—and this was not something I expected, and it was not Christmas or my birthday.

Gently I moved aside the tissue paper and pulled out a beautiful night dress, an exact replica of the one I had taken from the charity donation bag and was cherishing. I hugged it, kissed it gently, and said, "Now this is the best thing I have." Laying it out on the bed, I went in search of Ms. Smith who was in her night chair—there was a particular chair she sat in only at night before going to bed. I said, "Thank you, I also appreciate you," and I leaned over and gave her a kiss on the cheek. As I was leaving the room she said, "Rose, you have treated me and my home with profound respect. You are a kind soul. God bless you, my child." The genuine motherly love that came from her was comforting; I felt pure love in that moment, and I gently put my precious gift on my dresser and treated it like a souvenir.

Meeting A Helpmate

The next day at school, there was the young man I had most recently met in my class looking for me and made his way over to where I was sitting. I felt shy and did not want to make friends with him for all the obvious reasons, and I did not want to keep lying about my life, I just wanted to be left alone to choose my battles. I had purchased a few pieces of inexpensive clothing while shopping with Ms. Smith, and with the few she had given me, I was halfway presentable and not the 'eye sore' I was before. He eventually introduced himself, he said, "I'm Demetry, I am pleased to meet you." I was not interested in meeting him, but later I found a friend in him. He reminded me of Zan—he listened to me intently when I spoke, and he looked me in my eyes and showed a lot of concern. I shared a little about my life with him when the classes ended after the three months. He wanted to keep in touch, but I did not have a phone of my own and I was not going to give out Ms. Smith's phone to anyone, except to my mom who called about twice a month. I took his number and promised to call.

One day while Ms. Smith was out for a few hours at the beauty shop, I decided to call him, and he was so happy to hear from me. He asked when he could see me, and I told him I would be going to the mall by the school for ice cream that Saturday afternoon, I told him I go there on Saturdays after I leave the library. This was my Saturday schedule. He said he would come and meet me there. We met and sat in a public area and talked for a long time about nothing. I was perfecting the art of talking about everything except the details of my life. Then we planned to meet the next Saturday afternoon. I did not go the next Saturday but went to the same spot a few weeks later for my ice cream treat which was my reward to myself at the end of each week. As I got my treat and was looking for a spot to sit, there he was, sitting on the same bench where we last met. He told me he came every Saturday hoping I would come. I was impressed with his interest in seeing me again, so I sat with him for a while. I started building trust in him but kept my distance. He never forced anything on me, he said he found me fascinating and loved the quiet way I saw the world.

By this time, I was going through my divorce. The man I was married to had given me an ultimatum that if I did not return by a certain time to the matrimonial home, he would cut me out of his life and divorce me. I told him whatever he wanted to do was fine with me because even if I did come home, it would not be to him. I could not tell him that if I came home, it would be to Zan. I could never hurt anyone intentionally and that would be an intentional hurt. That was not in me. He proceeded to get a divorce on the grounds of desertion and published it in the local newspaper to expose me—maybe his destiny in life was to put me through shameful situations—and that if I did not return by a certain date; which was thirty days of publishing that record; I would lose all my rights to my share in our home and custody to my child. I did not respond to him or his threats. I was hoping that the divorce would go through as quickly as possible so I could lose my ties to him. The thirty days came and went, and no divorce was issued.

That man I was married to realized I was an asset to him in managing his home life while he enjoyed the freedom of a single life. He had seen me as fragile and needed his shelter and he felt I could not survive without him—he had said that. He felt I was his property and decided to make a trip to look for me and take me back home. My mom shared this in a conversation as she had learned it. So, I went into hiding and stopped my ice cream treats. My classes were over, so I was not out in the evenings. I stayed on location with Ms. Smith and only went out with her to church and food shopping and was looking over my shoulder at those outings. Through the very few contacts I kept, I learned that he did come but could not find me.

It was close to a year since I was living on my own in England and six of those months have been with Ms. Smith. The climax at this point was that he decided to go ahead with the divorce after his threat did not work and he could not find me on his visit. I continued going back to my ice cream spot but did not see Demetry. I thought that maybe he moved on to other things, and that was okay.

On the one-year anniversary of being away from home, and on my own, my mother called on our regular calls and told me the divorce was final. I felt free for the first time in a long time. I did not get anything from the divorce settlement, but I was happy. I was never one for material stuff. And had opened my bank account and was making deposits, saving my money, and planning what to do next with my life.

Before the ink could dry on the divorce papers, I received a letter from the district tax office asking me to come in with my legal permit authorizing me to work so they could allocate the right taxes to my file. There was a deadline attached to the letter to respond by a particular date. This was a serious situation, and many people were punished by being sent back to their country of origin. This would be detrimental to me. As the agency filed taxes for me, the system did not have the correct information to allocate the tax funds, so that pointed to me not having the right papers, or that I filled out something incorrectly. I got by this far, and now some more fears were facing me.

Full of fear, I felt I had to trust someone, or I would lose my mind. The only people in my life at this time were Ms.

Smith and Demetry. I had to decide to survive. Should I run away and go into hiding from fear of being caught; if I did, I will have to keep running and hiding, or go to another country where I know absolutely no one and start over. Can I change my identity, what am I supposed to do? I just want to live and have a decent existence—that is all I am asking. God, please do not forget me, please. I was at another crossroad.

The weekend after I had no desire for a treat but thought maybe I would go for a walk just to see if Demetry were hanging around out there. I was now free from that man I was married to but caught in another trap that might be just as bad.

I had completed my computer classes and felt good about that. I wanted to go back to school but that was a distant possibility. With the current situation at hand, I was distraught. In a strange place with no friends because I would not call the one friend here a friend, she was someone I knew, and I appreciated her opening her door and sheltering me when she did. I had no family here, and I was totally exposed and vulnerable and I felt sick. This is where I can end up in a garbage heap if I run away and must stay in hiding and can never say who I am or have the right papers to get a job—any job. Without the right papers, the only two things left for me to do are beg or sell my body. The latter could never happen—death would be a better choice. I felt the walls were closing in on me.

I went for a walk with the intention of calling Demetry from a phone booth if I did not see him at the ice cream shop. While walking I was looking at the world and wondering why I was in this condition in life. Why is my life so complicated when all I ever wanted was so simple, to be a nun and help people? I said to God, "Wanting to serve you has caused me all this pain. What am I to do, what am I doing wrong, please correct me?" I found solace in working for Ms. Smith because that was helping someone. Assisting in her garden and managing her home was all I knew. Ms. Smith had grown to really care for me and treated me like family. I was wondering if I should tell her of my dilemma, or should I call Zan, maybe he would tell me to come home and let us pick up where we left off. But I did not want to be a weak woman running to Zan for him to rescue me, he had already done that.

Demetry crossed my mind, and I crossed the street to use the phone booth. I dialed his number but no answer. I stood there not knowing if I should go left or right, so I walked to the corner thinking wherever the light turned green, that was the direction I would go, and the light turned green, so I went right.

Never thinking I would see Demetry again I continued walking in dismay. I lost track of myself as I got lost in my thoughts when someone called my name and I recognized the voice, but I was puzzled. Faith would have it that I walked right past Demetry and did not see him, but he saw me. He was going in the direction of the ice cream shop. "Hi Rose, how are you?" I was startled! I was sad and confused. He noticed that something was wrong. I looked at him and said, "I have a lot going on." He asked if I wanted to talk, and I shrugged my shoulders. I was at a breaking point; he stretched his hands out and hugged me and I felt safe in that moment in his arms. Since my last hug from Zan and the gentle welcoming hug from Ms. Smith, this was the first hug I have had. He said he was thirsty and so was I. So, we went to a fast-food place about two blocks away for a snack and sat down.

While sitting there with him, I thought I had nothing to lose by sharing my predicament, and I did. I spoke for a while, and he listened attentively. Then he said, "You only have one problem, and I will solve that if you let me!"

He said, "You need to get married to get your legal

papers to work. If you get married to someone who is a citizen of this country, it will take a few months for you to get your permit to work and that would allow you to do all the things you want to do; go to school and do everything that you cannot do now. I am here as you know, just out of graduate school and planning the next move in my professional life. I do not have any special person in my life, and I will be happy to marry you and get you straighten out."

I was floored!

Who is this angel? He went on to say, "The sooner the better. You have nothing to worry about. I will take you to meet my uncles so you will know where they live and their families and that should make you comfortable to move forward with this venture."

In the next few weeks, I met his uncles and their families and was introduced as his girlfriend. They all liked me, and I liked them too. We planned how we would marry and keep it a secret, and as soon as the paperwork was completed, we would secretly divorce.

One month later, I was married for the second time. Just the two of us at the justice of the *peace, and yet again, it was not a real marriage. But one that would serve a great purpose to support the choices I made to run away from the first marriage and to make something of my fractured life. One difference about this marriage was I respected Demetry. He was my friend, we never consummated that marriage; it was his favor to me, his friend. It was an understanding.*

I continued residing with Ms. Smith, and he continued living on his own and with his uncles. We would meet for ice cream and visit each other as we did before. Because of the marriage, I gave him the number for Ms. Smith and told him only to call if he absolutely had to. We grew closer as friends and learned to trust each other in a deep way. I liked him because it was not a relationship to caused me pain, physically, mentally, or emotionally. I started looking forward to seeing him; and I looked forward to laughing—something I did not know much of. He told me I was like a child; I had a childlike manner and innocence even though I was grown. He realized that I was not street-smart, and he started being protective of me in a very nice way.

The time was approaching for my paperwork to be called up for a hearing, and he said to me, "Rose, soon you will have all your papers and you will be free to move on and do the things you want to do. But before we show up for the appointment with the authorities, we should spend some time rehearsing different things and be comfortable showing affection toward each other in public." So, we rehearsed and got things lined up. He realized that he had grown close to me and really cared for me. One day he said to me, "Rose, I cannot deal with the thought of you moving away from me. I would love to date you for real."

I had grown to really care for him, and at times felt I loved him, but it was not the same love he confessed he had for me, he had a romantic love for me, but I did not love him the way I loved Zan. He was sincere and honest, and I liked that. Also, he treated me with respect and never tried to force himself on me. I felt a bit of excitement about the idea of dating since I had never really dated. Let us say, have a boyfriend. But reality stepped in and reminded me that I had some complications in my life and that I should not bring him into it. I had a lot of things I wanted to do and achieve and a lot of serious issues to deal with.

My list of things to do, and things I want to achieve, was a long list. I told him I could not be what he wanted, as I was badly damaged and needed to focus on making a life for me, I needed to find my way in this world. I really appreciated what he was doing for me thus far. But I cannot date him.

We finally showed up for our appointment before two barristers at-law for our hearing. I was very nervous, but Demetry was comfortable and encouraged me to relax because everything would be fine. Together we made a great-looking couple, and he had no problem showing me love before the eyes of the world, and I was comfortable receiving his affection because it felt pure. Everything went smoothly, the paperwork was approved on the spot, and the documentation was mailed to us.

We went to dinner to celebrate and unbeknown to him I had a thank-you gift for him. I felt he was struggling financially so I had put some money together to give him as a gift to thank him for his kindness. Initially, he refused and was reluctant to take anything from me, he indicated that he wanted to take care of me, but I wanted to show my appreciation. After some persuasion from me, he finally accepted, and I felt good because no good deed should go unpaid in some way. I wanted to do more than just say 'Thank You.' He kept bringing up the question of dating and I kept giving him all the reasons why it was not the best idea.

A Taste of Freedom

We kept seeing each other the same way for a few more months.

Now, I was free to really exhale and to make plans and execute them. I wanted a place of my own, a job, my child, and to start my education. As we continued our friendship and good caring conversations, our friendship grew to another level, and I shared my life goals in more detail. I was very open and honest about what I wanted and why. I shared I never wanted another child, and I did not want to be a wife, after not being able to live my dream and the life I wanted, I was settling for a single life, and that was the happiness I was moving toward.

I expressed to Demetry that I could not be a wife to a regular man, the core of me did not want that and I did not want to disappoint him by dating and moving in that direction, and I did not want to compromise anymore. He listened attentively and seemed to understand. His understanding made me feel free to tell him about my convent experience that caused my pregnancy and my first marriage.

As I told Demetry about the depth of my life, he cried, and I cried too because there was so much pain there. He hugged me for a long time and then he apologized for my lost dream and said he respects me even more; and now after knowing this, some things make sense, this is the piece of the puzzle he was missing. He said there was something different about me and he could not understand what it was but now he knows.

He shared that he was glad he followed his heart and helped me the way he did, and he will always be there for me regardless of my decision. I could not disclose my affair to him about Zan. That was very uncomfortable for me to talk about to anyone, I went to confessions about it and that was a part of my heart I could not share. That was my secret, and I chose to keep it that way.

Zan was on my mind constantly at this time because I could now travel, and I thought about making a trip home to see my mom and child and him. With this new freedom, I could make that trip and be able to come back and continue with my desires, but something kept me from Zan, from calling and touching base. There is much guilt on my part on the way I did not allow him to follow me when I left the man I was married to and was heading for where I am now. Zan was devastated when I left, and I am so sorry I left him that way. I could not stand the pain that existed between us, so I never called. Also, I do not know what is happening in his life, is there someone special in his life now? I am sure he has moved on and I cannot deal with that. So, I put aside making a visit to see my mom and child because the man I was married to would have to be involved and I was not ready to deal with him. At least not yet.

A few times Demetry attempted to show me his affection by hugging me in a way that would lead to further romance, and I always pushed him away gently; but after that conversation about me wanting to be a nun, he kept a distance as a matter of respect, and I appreciated that. I was moving on with my plans and we needed to start talking about divorcing and going our separate ways; I wanted to always remain a good friend, a special person in his life. I loved him but not in the way he wanted. Every time the subject came up about divorcing, he would say, "Let's discuss this at another time, not now."

My life with Ms. Smith was coming to an end and I explained some things to her which she understood, she wished me well on my ventures to make an independent life for myself.

When I found my first job, I was still residing with her, she was so excited and happy for me, she said she saw lots of potential in me and knew in her heart I would do very well.

When I started my job search, I was proud to put my computer training on my application. A few companies replied and I was so delighted to receive their responses. I had a few interviews, and one of the companies had a position for their owner and president and they wanted me to meet him. I was not comfortable with that position, but the placement officers I met insisted that I meet with him. This was a very well-known prestigious company, and I was applying for an entry-level position where I would have an opportunity to move up. I nervously met him, and he was sure I was who he wanted to support his office—I was hired on the spot. This was the highest-level administrative support position in the company.

Literally shaking, I walked to the corner where I could exhale from what had just happened. I had an indescribable feeling of gratitude. God gave me so much more than I was asking for. It would have been my heart's delight to get an entry-level position and work my way to something higher, but I was immediately placed at the top of what I could only imagine. The pay was more than I could understand as I was accustomed to a maid's pay; now my pay was considered mid-level executive with lots of great benefits along with an expense account—this I could not comprehend. My thanks to God could not stop and a few tears of joy and gratitude did take center stage.

A week later I started my new job, nervous and in disbelief.

When I reported for work, I was directed by the receptionist where to go, and to my surprise—there was an office with my name on the door, I entered what was beyond my expectations. This office was next to the president's office, and it was just a smaller version of his. It was very impressive.

A month later I found a flat of my own. When I told Ms. Smith, she gave me a blank cheque and told me to furnish it as I pleased—but with my simple way of thinking and a modest nun's heart, I got only what I needed and nothing more. She was upset that I did not really shop. Not only that, but I also wanted to get the things I needed, one thing at a time—and modestly.

Ms. Smith had a lot of separation anxiety about me moving on and asked me to assist her in finding a replacement, or at least be available to interview the next person, and I did. She said if her flat was not rented she would offer it to me, and I told her I would like that.

The first night in my flat on my own bed, I slept in my souvenir night dress, and I felt so good I did not want that evening to end. I felt like a special human being, and I was full of joy with my newfound freedom.

I continued going to church with Ms. Smith, she was always delighted to see me, and I would also visit her sometimes to see that she was okay; I did a few things for her that a daughter would do for a mom. I saw that her clothes were properly fixed and my sewing skills, from way back, came in handy for those fixings—she was always amazed at the things I could do.

A Proposal

We were approaching a long holiday weekend and Demetry wanted me to come to his hometown to meet his parents. I hesitated, and then decided to go. His family was excited about me based on all he had shared with them, and they loved me immediately, as I did them. We had dinner with his parents and other relatives then his mom gave me a tour of their home. I was treated like a celebrity.

Demetry was from a small town also. He took me for a drive showing me the schools he attended and stopped by a few friends who still lived in the town. I loved the tree-lined streets, the well-manicured lawns, and the well-planned communities. At every few blocks, there were small stores, a post off, a pub, and a community hall. Most of these conveniences were within walking distance of the community they served. There were a lot of similarities in the way we were brought up so many islands apart.

When it was time for me to retire for the evening, he escorted me to my room to be sure I was comfortable. This room was next to his parents' bedroom, it was his sister's room, she had moved to her own flat in another town where she had a wonderful job. I knew he would not disrespect his parents or me. So, I entered the room and turned to say good night to him, but noticed his body was going downward and I thought something was wrong with him, but he was going on his knees and with the door wide open he proposed to me!

He said, "Rose, you have given my life purpose, I would like to give you my life and all the love I have for the rest of my life, would you marry me?"

Oh my God, what is this, what should I do? I cannot hurt his feelings, and I cannot say 'yes' either. I cannot be a wife; I cannot be married again. I do not want to!

I pulled him into the room and pushed the door in, not locking it, but for a bit of privacy so no one could hear me, I sat him on the chair in the bedroom and I said, "I cannot accept this proposal. I do not want to bear or mother another child; I am already compromising with the life I have, and I cannot compromise anymore. I do not want to." He said he understood and was aware of my concerns and did not want me to compromise, he just wanted me in his life, as his wife. He said, "I never asked you for a child. I just want you as my wife."

Considering my life, which consisted of him and Ms. Smith, put me in deep thought. He was all I had for a while, and he proved to be a friend. Thus far we have not had a sexual relationship. This was a clean friendship with lots of caring from both sides but very personal. I felt we were soulmates on another level and maybe I should think this through.

Another Crossroad

This proposal caught me off guard and I was not sure what to do. It was not the direction I wanted to go—I was confused. I told him I needed to think and have further discussions with him. Before he left the room, I said, "I love you, and I don't think I could be a wife to you or anyone."

I did not sleep a wink that night. There were so many scenarios running in my head but what bothered me most of all was having more children. I also thought about Zan. I would not compromise on having children. No one was opening that door. A wife maybe, in a Godly marriage, I would consider. As the next day started, I was heavy with all the thoughts of the night and wondering in my mind 'What about Zan?' This should be our time, perhaps I should call him and see what he is doing with his life and then decide what to do. If he is not available and has moved on, then maybe I could get his blessing on this proposal. But I still cannot call him. I do not know why. Maybe because I want him and him only and I never want to hear anything else, and the possibility exists that he may have moved on. I know for sure that if he did, my place would be reserved. There is no doubt about that, just as his place is reserved for me.

Demetry and I spoke about all the scenarios I had about life. The scenario about children was the most difficult because there was no room to negotiate because I would not compromise. And the only marriage I would have been a Godly one.

With a lot of reluctance, I accepted Demetry's proposal. He was overjoyed and somehow in disbelief, I think he was expecting me to turn him down totally, but he had been so good to me, so why not? I cannot be a nun anymore and Zan and I may not be—and something is keeping me from communicating with him.

I called my mom, and he went out to his parents who were so excited to let them know we were going to get married. They were screaming and jumping for joy! My parents were both on the phone and were happy because I was moving my life in a good direction. Demetry spoke to my parents telling them he would support me, and all my dreams, and that he would take excellent care of me. He told them how much he loved and cared for me, and they must not worry. His parents spoke to my parents. When I went back to the phone my mom was shedding tears of joy. She said I prayed for you to find happiness—I am so happy for you. She said she felt I was in good hands.

Demetry's grandfather was a pastor, with his own small church right there in town, so we decided that is where we would get married. Since I was a stranger and did not have anyone, I felt that was the best thing to do. And the fact that we were already married, it was having a wedding ceremony to renew our vows and start a real marriage.

Before the weekend was over my life had taken on a new meaning and a new direction. I had new plans and lots to do.

Demetry and his parents offered to provide everything for the wedding. My only focus was getting my wedding gown and attire and showing up.

We needed more space for the two of us, so we got a larger flat in the same complex where I had my flat and started setting up for our new life. It took some adjusting for me, but I was having fun. He was fun to be with and he showed me lots of love. I found joy during this time in my life, and I laughed a lot. I kept going to church and staying close to God, and every day I thought of Zan. I felt I needed to tell him what I was doing but I still could not contact him. It amazed me how much Demetry reminded me of Zan, and I liked that. It was like I had a part of Zan with me. At times when I thought about Zan I would get sad, but I never said what I was sad about. And besides Zan, I had a lot that could make me sad; at times I felt homesick, sometimes I felt like running away to another country and enrolling in a convent as someone who had no one and wanted to serve but what lies would I build that life on? And all the time I missed my child. I was always deep down conflicted.

A Real Wedding

The date had finally arrived, and I had my beautiful

wedding gown which I made myself. All the skills I had learned about sewing were put into practice, and I had the most beautiful wedding gown I had ever seen, made of cream bridal satin, with matching lace and satin ribbons of different widths and cream pearl buttons. I designed a gown that was covered with lace over satin from the waist up separated by a wide satin ribbon and gathered from the waist to the bottom which went to the floor. The ribbon around my waist was decorated and draped to my side with pearl buttons in the design of two 'signs of the cross' on each end. One cross for each marriage, this was not a real wedding, it was the renewing of our vows as a token for us moving forward with God's blessings and doing it in a church. The crosses were put together by pearl buttons on satin with tiny matching ribbon trim. I could not find a pair of satin shoes in the color I wanted, so I bought a pair of white satin shoes in the style I liked and had them coloured to match my gown. I borrowed a beautiful pearl necklace from Ms. Smith, and I bought a blue garter for my stockings. I had something old, something new, something borrowed, and something blue. I packed my gown and all the trimmings and was ready for my trip. Ms. Smith had offered me the chance to have my wedding at her home and I would have loved that, but it was appropriate to have it in Demetry's hometown in his grandfather's church. She said, "I will be in my night chair at the time you are taking your vows. That is my 'prayer' chair. I do most of my praying at night in that chair, and I will sit there for the duration of your ceremony. If I could travel, I would not miss your wedding for anything."

Demetry went home a week before the wedding, and I followed a few days after. I took my gown properly wrapped on the plane with me, I could not take the chance to check it in and have it get lost somewhere. When I arrived and Demetry picked me up from the airport, he said, "I have a nice surprise for you!" I said, "Everything would be a surprise because I will be seeing everything that was prepared for the first time so everything would be a surprise," and he smiled. Arriving at his parents' home and to my surprise—to greet me was my mom—my mom! I was so happy! I loved having her there so much because at times I felt I had fallen off a tree somewhere and did not belong anywhere so to have my own mom there at this special occasion was grand! My heart was happy. It was the best surprise—more than I could have imagined or expected. Demetry said she had been there for the last two days, and he was spending each moment with her, and they were very comfortable together.

The wedding was beautiful, and my new husband was handsome and happy. He made a fuss with me and my mom and said I was a carbon copy of her. During my time there, my mom and I had some time catching up on the events of our island, my child, and the man I was married to. Without knowing what role Zan played in my life, the afternoon at the wedding reception, she told me he was married, just light chatting about the Island. My heart sank—and I did everything possible to hide my feelings. I looked at my beautiful satin shoes and started playing with the satin ribbon on the side of my gown which held the beautiful pearl buttons and the two crosses. I was romancing those buttons and thinking that I had to deal with my life the way it is now with the choices I made. I did everything to hide my feelings. The place Zan held in my heart was reserved for him. No one could touch that. Now I have a genuinely nice husband who loves me, and I would make a life with him providing I could serve God in this new life. We had discussed the kind of marriage we were going to have in this compromising life I was continuing to live.

We went on a short honeymoon and that was the first time we got intimate. That was more difficult than I expected because I was one with Zan, one heart, one mind, one body. I had to learn patience with Demetry and with myself and that was a day-to-day effort. In that effort, I grew to love and appreciate Demetry and looked forward to my marriage with him.

After we got back from the honeymoon, the first thing we did was seek permission from the man I was married to so my child could visit to see what was possible. After much struggle and negative dialogue, my child visited for a few weeks during school vacation and did not like my new country, or my new husband. My child was brainwashed, and I felt a negative attitude that was unacceptable, but I did what was necessary to keep things pleasant. My child was at the age I was when I was wronged, and something about that was very disturbing and alive in my mind. I was seeing how much of a child I was when my life changed so sadly. However, I knew the value of education and my child's father had things set up nicely with a top boarding school on the Island, so I was not going to get in the way of that. Nonetheless, my life flashed before me many times during that visit, and after the vacation was over, I shared it with Demetry and told him I would address that issue one day, with that man. I absolutely must address it.

I focused on my other dreams and was accomplishing them one-by-one.

Demetry and I had now been married for about three years and had bought a beautiful older home which we spent much time refurbishing and decorating. Again, I designed a beautiful garden which amazed him. I felt contented with my life and was often in my garden when the weather permitted, sitting quietly, studying, as I was taking classes at the university to further my education. I would think of Zan often but was not saddened with thoughts of him now. Nonetheless, I wondered how my life would have been with him as my husband. I loved my new husband, but not the way I loved Zan. I had a passion for Zan. Demetry and I went to church regularly and enjoyed worshiping together, and he accompanied me to some volunteer activities for the church which made me happy.

We made a few friends through the years, mostly Demetry, and socialized with them from time to time. It was not easy for me to open up to strangers and befriend them. But I tried to be accommodating. Some of these friends were much into excessive alcohol drinking and parties. Which did not sit well with me especially when Demetry wanted to hang out in that crowd. This at times causes us to argue. He thought I wanted to control him, and he resented me because he said he could not control me. Through the marriage, whenever we argued a part of me would get very sad because the arguments were all unnecessary. I missed living a quiet life just praying and serving God—in other words, I missed the life I wanted after not being a nun, the life of quiet singleness and dignity, and serving church and community in some way. Now, I was serving a husband whom I found myself having to persuade on many occasions to put God first, and for us to pray together, and seek God's guidance. And I did not like that. Serving God should not be a struggle.

His friends were of the world. Many of them had children and were having babies, which gave Demetry the idea that we should join the crowd and have a baby, and this, he claimed, caused him to start drinking excessively and staying out late at night.

One night he told me he discussed our situation with some of his friends and his parents, and they thought I was selfish—which went from one problem to another. I would gently remind him of our conversation about children the night he proposed to me, but that made no difference to his newfound demand of me. I knew I was not going to compromise, so there was no need for an argument or discussion and as such, in a short time, our happy home was not so happy anymore.

Seven Years After Leaving Home

Demetry would not accept our initial agreement of me not having a baby. He met with lots of success and felt that now we could afford a child easily, and I would be able to stay home and raise our child, so he could and would not accept my wishes. These arguments led to a separation. I was enduring my second separation that may lead to divorce. A separation and divorce I did not want. I was contented to live out the rest of my life with Demetry.

It was not whether I stayed at home or not, it was that I did not want another child. He was also overwhelmed by his success and did not know how to handle the influx of women making themselves available to him, so he got involved in extramarital affairs and later I learned through the most terrifying way that his infidelity included prostitutes.

With my trusting way of thinking and knowing his success would keep him from home at times, I did not question a lot of things that did not add up. I knew he was struggling with the idea of us having a child and I thought that one day he would give up the idea and we would continue with our lives as we had started—with love, care, and respect.

At home relaxing on a day off, Demetry called and said, "You need to see your doctor." I asked why. He said, "Because I went out with a prostitute and got infected."

The phone went dead silent—that same loud silence I had heard before—many, many years before, and after a while, I hung up.

I was sitting at the end of the bed when I received

Demetry's call and about an hour later, I was crawling from inside a closet that I had torn up. I lost it. I threw everything out of the closet and must have been hitting the wall because my hands were bruised and bloody. Everything was thrown off the vanity. I was suffocating from the strong scents of cologne and perfume that I had thrown into the walls and splashed all over the room. I would have set him free to find the right woman since I was not the one. I told him upfront I could not go this route. Why did he have to hurt me this way, why?

I grabbed a pillow off the bed and screamed at the top of my lungs until I started coughing uncontrollably. I would rather die than live like this, how messed up is this kind of life? What caliber of man would do something like this? This is horrible, maybe I should just be a prostitute because this life I am trying to live is not working. I hated myself in that moment and I hated that man I was married to.

I went to the bathroom and took a hot shower, which did not end until all the hot water ran out. In that shower, I kept saying all I wanted to do was be a nun and that was taken from me. Then I accepted my marriage to Demetry to live a respectable life and now this is the result—what am I supposed to do, what am I doing wrong? Lord, I cannot take it anymore, let me come home and be with you, please.

I stepped out of the shower with blisters all over my body from the hot water, I could not touch my skin because it was sensitive, sore, and tender. So, I looked for my souvenir from Ms. Smith, that soft beautiful night dress, and put it on my wet body, picked up my Bible, and went to my garden where I stayed until the darkness of the evening matched the feelings in my soul. I did not hear the music of the leaves that day and the flowers did not turn to face me, I was too sad and the cry in my heart was too loud to hear the music of the leaves. Demetry did not come home that night and that was a good thing.

What was left of me died that day, literally. The humiliation of visiting my doctor was heartbreaking, not to mention the horror of going through certain tests and waiting for results. I told Demetry he should avoid me and occupy any area of the house where I was not. I found that easy to do since I had that training and experience from my first marriage. There was nothing to speak to Demetry about so, I said nothing to him ever again. That was the end of us.

I told God he could take me back to be with him because nothing was working for me, and I did not know what to do anymore.

Eventually, after much intervention from his parents and my mom, we sought counseling, and I worked very hard at forgiving him but found it impossible to reconcile. Forgiveness was not that hard, but reconciliation was impossible. The hurt was too much to deal with and I was horrified about the diseases I could have been exposed to. It became clear to me that he was unfaithful many times—this was the only time he got caught. I could not trust him, and I could not combine forgiveness with reconciliation, so we went our separate ways.

That separation led me into an indescribable bout of anxiety and depression, and I lost myself again. There was no will to live, and I did not have the energy to focus on life. Excessive showering and sleeping were the only things I could do without much effort. I felt unclean all the time. I wore what was in front of me whether it was soiled or not, I found a way of wearing my hair that did not need much maintenance, and it showed. It took a lot of effort to get out of bed in the mornings and to go to work and function. I would go to work and, when I got home, I took a shower and went to bed. I used a lot of sleeping aids from over the counter to keep hiding from reality and to keep me sleeping. I felt I solved a lot of my issues while sleeping.

Demetry occupied the basement of the house when he was there, our paths hardly ever crossed as he stayed out of the house most of the time. After months of feeling lost and not knowing what to do, I woke up one day with a burst of energy and before the sun went down that day, I rented a flat, my own flat.

There were some beautiful garden-style flats in a neighboring town that I had always admired; so, I visited and was surprised there was a vacancy for a flat I was comfortable with, so I rented it, a small flat like the first one I had. I came home with the keys to my new flat and started packing what I wanted to take with me. There was an elegant furniture store I had seen close to the trains I used on my commute to work, and I decided to visit. In that furniture store, I bought everything I needed for my new flat and arranged to have it delivered in two weeks. During that time, I took the few things I needed along with my clothing to my new flat and waited for the delivery of my furniture. My boss knew something was wrong and I decided to have a conversation with him about my marriage coming to an end. In that conversation, I told him I would need to take some time off to get settled in another flat, and he approved.

I sorted myself out in my new flat and laid around for a few days getting accustomed to my new home. And immediately after that, I found a therapist and started therapy.

During this time, I was still in school but was failing my classes, I could not concentrate, and nothing was making sense to me, everything needed more effort and energy than I had. There were times I felt suicidal, and it felt like a relief just thinking about it. But I could not dwell on that sort of negativity because I always had a solid relationship with God, and I knew he would never leave or forsake me even though I felt forsaken by the way things were. My faith in God kept me grounded.

Being Anchored

Leaving the neighborhood, I had grown to love, the friends, my church family, my home, and my garden were not easy. Embarrassed again to face my church and my church life, I was pushed to wear a veil of deceit and I told untruths to cover what I did not want to talk about. I felt so unworthy that I was separated from a second husband, I felt judged, and it was hard to speak the truth. I had an overwhelming feeling of failure so I started missing church or would go to a different service where I did not know much of the members. Then after a few months, I found a new church closer to my flat which I enjoyed.

Being anchored and staying faithful to God was a very private journey for me—it kept me on my knees. It became clear to me that the night Demetry proposed to me I should have followed that inner voice and stayed on my path to live the life I wanted, a single life serving God. But my thoughts were overshadowed by his kindness—and I went the route to marry him thinking it would be a continuation of what we had. However, I knew Jesus loved me and I had that special relationship with him and was able to go to him in that 'turtle's shell' and always came out knowing things would work out.

During my separation, I felt I was avoided by many, and those who did not avoid me said all the wrong things. I was broken, and the horizontals were telling me to move on since the only way to heal was to find another partner and go out and have fun. Some of the contacts I had at my job would invite me to parties and other functions for which I had no interest. That was like telling an injured person to shake off the injury and forget the pain. I did not want another partner or a party, and I did not want to suppress the pain and ignore my issues. In the lowest moments of my distress, those were never my options, I went back to basics. I found peace and comfort in reading, sewing, taking care of myself, and getting my needed rest. I even started cooking certain dishes I had never cooked and prepared before for two reasons: to occupy some of my time and to eat the right foods. I cried a lot and I wanted to be alone to cry when I needed to cry, and then there came a time when the tears did not come as much.

Being and staying anchored is a painful process. People ask, why does it have to be so painful to move through this process? And I think because that is the only way we learn and grow.

I had to drop out of school to focus on getting well with the intention of returning later. This was a time-out for me. I was depressed and despondent, but I kept my job and daily work schedule, and I did therapy. My therapist recommended many different things for me to do; like hitting pillows, screaming in pillows; writing letters that I will not mail – writing my feelings out, and so on. When I left my therapy session, I would stop by a floral shop close to the train station and buy myself roses twice a week. This helped me tremendously but there were times I would fluctuate with up and down emotions.

Weeks and weeks into working on myself, I picked up my mail one afternoon feeling a bit down and despondent—just rushing to get home to be in my comfort zone to drink a glass of wine and relax. In my mail, I noticed a strange envelope. It was a different kind of envelope addressed to me from familiar handwriting. I kept looking at it and reading it as I went to the door. I went into my flat, turned over the piece of mail and there was the name of the sender written upside down on the back of the envelope—it was from Zan. Oh my God!

Just seeing his name on the envelope in his handwriting made me forget how sad I was at that moment; I leaped for joy, dropped all the other pieces of mail, my keys, and my pocketbook, kicked off my shoes, went to the dining room, and poured two glasses of wine; one for me and one for Zan. I got comfortable on the sofa with his letter—feeling like a child at Christmas. I kissed the letter where he wrote my name, and I kissed where he signed his. Then I opened the letter.

My Darling Rose,

> *After visiting your mom and learning that you are now separated from your husband, I decided to ask for your address to contact you. I was so excited to drop you these lines to see how you are and to establish contact with you. As you might have heard, I did get married to Hanah, whom I had mentioned I met before you left home, but we are now divorced.*
>
> *Rose, you took my heart when you left so there was nothing to give her; I was a shell. She said I was looking for someone else when I looked at her, but she had no idea who I was longing for. After a few years, she decided to let me go, and I accepted our separation and divorce without a fight.*
>
> *I have relived the moments I shared with you through the years and nothing with no one could compare. I have looked for you in everyone and could not find what I was looking for. After my divorce, I continued and completed my medical studies to dedicate the rest of my life to helping the sick. I needed to find a new purpose for my life.*
>
> *I miss you; my soul misses you. I need to be in touch with you. I have never stopped loving you, and I never will. Please respond and let me know how you are. I sincerely care about your well-being.*

I love you always.

Zander

I felt so connected to him in those moments reading his letter and I missed him too; my soul missed him. I cried for my heartstring that was tied to his. I held the letter to my chest, and I hugged myself with that letter on me imagining what it would be like to be hugged and comforted by him. Then I picked up his glass of wine and went on with the evening which was different from the ones I could remember in the recent past, I was joyful—there was a smile on my heart.

As I lay in bed that night, I knew I would never let Zan out of my life again, ever. I was not sure if I wanted a romantic relationship again, for I had my doubts about those types of relationships since my experiences have been painful. But I wanted a friendship with Zan. I needed a friendship with him. After basking in the thought of him for a few nights and days, not knowing what to tell him and how long would such a response be, I responded.

My Zan,

There are no words to express the joy your letter has brought me. I received it when I needed it most. Since I left home my life has been one adventure after another, not that it was anything less adventurous while I was at home. Again, I am at a crossroads and must make some hard decisions. But with God's guidance and my faith in Him, I am hanging on.

I have missed you terribly and I have kept you in my heart over the years and have always prayed for your happiness and well-being. It would be my heart's desire to be in touch with you and to rekindle our friendship.

Do write to me again soon.

I love you,

Rose

When I completed his letter, I would put on lipstick and kiss where I signed my name—leaving a beautiful imprint. Somewhere for him to kiss when he receives my letter, this became part of the ritual.

I stayed committed to my therapy sessions and during the next month after communicating with Zan, I was feeling a bit better—my spirits were lifted. My life's vibration was raised. I continued fixing my flat and was doing nice things for myself. Every Friday afternoon after my therapy, I would purchase a larger bouquet of roses than the ones I purchase in the week to keep my company over the weekend. The soul cannot flourish without beauty, and I did not have a garden—so flowers were the next best thing, and they did wonders for me.

It was joyful writing to Zan, and I experienced an equal amount of joy receiving his letters. Each time I received a letter it was like a treat; I would go through the same ritual I did the day I got his first letter. The shoes would be kicked off, the pocketbook thrown out of my way, the other pieces of mail set aside for later attention, I would fix two glasses of wine, get comfortable, kiss where he wrote my name and where he was, and then open his letter.

This went on for about a year until my divorce was final.

The finalization of my divorce from Demetry made me sad thinking about the reality of how things went in the marriage when it had started out so well, so pure. Demetry felt I was not entitled to anything because I was not from his country and might have an inheritance on my Island. I did not fight for anything, as I was never one who had attachments to material stuff but that was not right, nor was it fair. But I made it ok. In my heart, I was always a nun and what do nuns really have? Nonetheless, I should get what I worked for and what I was entitled to. This was my second divorce and again I was left empty-handed. I walked away from that divorce broken financially but I could feel the hands of God working in my life; each day I was getting stronger and stronger in my emotions and my career was doing fine. Rekindling with Zan was the best thing that could have happened to me at that stage of my life—it brought me pure joy.

After my divorce, Zan wanted me to visit him, and initially, I wanted to go but was reluctant because I was still weak for him— and I was still fragile and broken. I was getting better day by day, but I was not strong enough to visit and be with him. My heart could not deal with any additional emotional pain. I knew Zan would not hurt me, but I knew it would be too painful seeing and being with him. So, I declined, which was just as painful, or maybe worse. When I told him, I was declining his offer, he cried, and I cried too. After a long conversation about life and us, he said, "What I offered you at the beginning of our relationship, I am offering you now—the ball is in your court!"

I continued school after a one-year lapse and was able to focus on making the grades, while holding my job, which promoted me with very nice financial increases. I felt God was repaying me for some of the financial losses. Many of my thoughts went into figuring out what I needed to do going forward to finally carve out and find my way in the world. I tried to understand what I did wrong and what I should have done differently because I did not want the results I was getting; I was tired of failing.

What always bothered me was how my simple desire in life got so distorted and complicated, and to this point, it had not turned around in my favor. It was clear I needed a different approach if I wanted to see different results. I knew that within me was the power to stop the things that had consumed me and caused me pain up to this point. Weighing the pros and cons of life and the choices I now have, my heart wanted to retire from the mainstream of life and go on a personal sabbatical from the horrors of romance and relationships. If one has a broken bone or some other sort of physical injury there would be a certain amount of time needed for it to heal; a broken bone would need a cast and I had serious invisible wounds, I needed to heal my wounds. I needed to heal my broken life. I could not afford to hurt this way anymore.

Personal Sabbatical

I took a break from relationships to really find myself. It felt good to get off the treadmill of pain and confusion. I was tired of failing, of disappointments, of compromising and being forced to compromise, and settling and never winning.

Now late twenties, I felt old and worn-out like someone who had lived a much longer life. My thoughts were going back and forth from one incident to another, so I decided to list my life's major events, and this is what they looked like:

Sexually hurt at fourteen.

Kicked out of the convent at fifteen.

Had a baby at fifteen.

Married to the enemy at sixteen.

Had an adulterous affair at twenty.

Ran to another country at twenty-two.

Divorced at twenty-three.

Remarried at twenty-three.

Divorced again at twenty-nine.

Approaching the age of twenty-nine, an age when most people are getting married for the first time, maybe having their first child, having fun, and finding themselves. I had already lived a full life and lost myself in the process, and at times, I lost my will to live. My life, since the age of fourteen, was a living hell. Now life was suffocating me. I was burdened down and needed time out.

A sabbatical was the only thing I could think of to restore me. Not another relationship and not another place or thing.

If I could still be a nun that would be the direction I would go because my heart was still there; but now it was more a case of running from reality, not the same reasons as that thirteen-year-old. My heart never changed from loving the Lord and wanting to serve him, now I could no longer be a nun, so the next best thing was for me to go on my sabbatical from relationships and nourish myself. My sabbatical is to live the way nuns lived, only that I kept a job. A life in selective seclusion and carve out the life I want for me.

My desire was always to help people, so I started by helping the one who needed the most help, me. I worked hard at finding myself and restoring my body, mind, and soul, not to mention my dignity and self-respect.

I treated myself like a baby, making sure I got enough rest, eating the right foods, and allowing myself to feel whatever feeling existed now. If I needed to cry, I cried; if I needed an ice cream cone, it got it; or whatever was the need at hand. I was gentle with myself. I decided to love myself and leave the rest of the world. I went back to living as if I were seven years old, back to basics, with that innocence. I said those original prayers religiously each day along with many others I added from my journey. I went back to the total trusting of a child, total surrender. No dating, not being out alone at night, if I had to work late there was always a car service to bring me home, I told anyone who was interested in talking to me, that I was married. I wore a wedding band—one I purchased that had no history to it, a band of my commitment to celibacy. I allowed no one in my personal space. I trusted no one, I lived like a nun.

Zan continued being in my corner, supporting me through the years in a loving way. He was always someone I could count on, and he was always very responsive to all my concerns. But we kept the relationship a long-distance one. We never visited each other, and that was my wish. My life moved leaps and bounds in every area, my church life was a happy life, my spirituality was stronger, my career flourished, I completed my studies, and traveled while doing wonderful things for me.

Twenty years later...

I have faced the authenticity of my life. Through the years I could not cope without my 'turtle's shell' or the cast that held me while I healed, but now, I am ready to face the world unveiled. I am healed.

***

This was the revelation of Rose facing the truth of her life, identifying the things that caused her profound pain, and how she moved away from those situations to find herself and her personal freedom. Rose had to move from the mainstream of life to find herself—she created her personal sabbatical. And she proved that being a nun was from the heart and she was a nun all along. That cruise served as her coming out from under the protection of the 'Turtle's Shell' and stepping out of the cast that held her while she healed.

She is transformed and ready to give back to the world in a different way, and in her terms. She is tired of the secrets and wants everything out in the open once and for all to let people know who she is—and how she suffered. Rose’s cup is full of life and running over with joy. She is totally healed from the wounds of the past—Rose is transformed.

Part 3

The Reveal

"Vanessa, let me reintroduce myself. I am Julia Rose. I am Rose!"

There again was that loud silence . . .

Vanessa was shocked… and, after holding her head she asked, "You are Rose, you went through all those horrific things?" I said, "Yes, I am Rose. Everything I told you is about me.

I have used the veil of Julia to get by in this world and not have to tell the truth of my life. Julia is my *imaginary* friend and confidant. I am Rose!"

She stretched out her arms and we hugged. Vanessa said, "God bless you; you are an exceptional person!" And her eyes filled with tears.

I could not risk telling my story in the beginning, I was so wounded and ashamed of my life and its complications; so, I gave Rose all the hurt and disappointments and I wore the veil of Julia. Too many questions were directed at Rose each time she attempted to come to the surface, and none were directed at Julia. I told people *'I am a nun'* whenever they asked me what I did; I never disclosed my life of hell, I took those things to confession. Those were my private struggles, and I kept all those things in the compartment with Rose—my silent purgatory. Julia had the freedom to live as she wanted and to accomplish her desires.

I had a deep need to get away from my everyday life and finally rethink all the events of my life and that is where the cruise came in. It was the appropriate thing to do, where I was not interrupted by anything or anyone. I arrived on the ship and had the best cabin with a private deck where I looked at the ocean for as far as my eyes could see, and that is where I stayed for most of the cruise. I unpacked one time and stayed with my thoughts as I needed. Everything came to the surface, I felt like I was underwater for a long time in a deep dive away from reality—and then I came up—shook the water off, and faced what was in front of me. I am now free to share the details of my life, something I could not do when I first met you.

A broken bone needs a cast to protect it while it heals—I needed a cast to protect me while I healed.

I desperately wanted to be a nun. I knew that from the age of seven—that was my only passion. I went away to the convent; got wounded; bore a child; and got married to my predator; and I never revealed who the predator was to the authorities or my community. I lived with the enemy for years; and while living with the enemy, I met and fell in love with the only man I ever loved, and still do, Zan.

My affair with Zan showed me what real love was, and how a man should love a woman. But that relationship was forbidden because I was still married. And the timing of our coming together did not allow us the freedom to explore our relationship and that brought unbearable emotional turmoil. I had to leave that situation to save myself.

I left my island for greater pastures…and was financially abused by a friend; I was homeless, and almost penniless, wearing rags, with my feet on the ground, working as a servant girl, and being on the run for not having a work permit or the proper legal papers which stopped me at times from collecting my paychecks.

Life was a living nightmare from that vicious night in my

convent life. Sometimes I wonder which was worse: living with the enemy or being on the run and facing these horrific challenges alone. The circumstances were different after I ran in search of another kind of life in comparison to what I ran from. By running away from living with the enemy I was able to make choices to improve my life and find myself.

The one passion I had to serve God and mankind was put into practice after my second divorce. I could not keep doing the same things and expecting different results, so I had to make a serious change. What I wanted to give to the world so desperately had to be given to me first—by me—and that is when I went on my personal sabbatical. I needed to fill my cup before I could help anyone fill theirs.

I chose excellence in the face of adversity by doing what was the Godly thing to do—making Godly choices and staying on the narrow path regardless of how hard those choices were.

My sabbatical was not easy, but it did not cause additional pain, it took the existing pain and dissolved it day-by-day, until one day there was no pain.

I redirected all my energies to myself, my education, and my career.

Now, after two decades of sabbatical life, I am truly healed from all the wounds of the past; the cast, the disguises, and the untruths are no longer needed. Zan and I have kept in touch through the years—we are very special friends with great respect and love for each other, but no romance. We have kept a long-distance friendship with no visits. We write and speak to each other regularly; and whenever he is venturing into anything, he calls me and I pray for him and offer my blessings, and he does the same for me. Of all the people I have met along life's journey, Zan is at the top of my list, and he was there from the first day I met him decades ago, he is my best friend and my soulmate.

One Regret

I never regretted having an affair, divorcing, or remarrying. My one regret was the evening I was taken advantage of, and never had my opponent face charges for what he did.

What he did traumatized me and ruined my life.

I should have exposed him to pay for his wrongdoing and face the consequences. But society was a barrier for me at the time. I was not comfortable telling anyone, I was scared and did not want to cause any further problems. I felt it was my fault and that was the way my society handled similar cases.

That is the one regret I have. I carried that burden alone and faced all the consequences, while my opponent enjoyed life and all its freedoms. That one incident was the springboard to all the other difficulties I endured. It sent my life spiraling out of control and turned me into a woman overnight at the age of fourteen, but I was just an injured child. Who knows, if I had the opportunity to fully develop and mature before having to deal with life's major issues, I might have met Zan and not fallen in love with him the way I did. But my life was so fractured and empty that I needed love desperately and he provided it. Without my dreams being violently taken away from me, I could have finished my convent education, got the full exposure to being a nun, and know for sure if that was what I really wanted. I was robbed of seeing the full picture of what could have been. And for that, I could see nothing else.

I have forgiven that night and its consequences and all that followed; I have forgiven myself, and I have forgiven what might have been. I now embrace what is—and it is wonderful living a life of freedom and joyfulness.

New Thoughts

Lately, I have been thinking of moving back to my island and giving back while living a semi-retired life. I ran from home under emotional stress and now feel a deep longing to go back and live my life with grace. I did not get the life I wanted, or the only man I ever loved, but I have a good life now, I made the best of what was left of me.

It was always compromising for me to live on another island, I never felt I totally belonged or was at home, I have a deep desire to go back to my island and live a simple life. I want to live differently now; I want to live on my terms with the schedule I set for myself. I want to embrace my happiness, freedom, simplicity, and joy—while living a life of quality.

It would also be wonderful to be close to my parents who are older now and to assist them in managing their lives.

These thoughts warmed my heart and I spoke to Zan about

my desire to move home and about going on a trip to see how my heart feels. He was elated! I also have friends and family there that I want to revisit and re-establish those relationships.

I have no desire to rekindle the romantic part of my relationship with Zan since I have grown accustomed to being by myself and that is where I find total joy. After being on both sides of the fence of life, I like this side better. This is the side I always wanted. Also, I want to keep the wonderful, special relationship with Zan the way it is.

After lots of thinking and careful planning, I have decided to go on a vacation to see how my heart feels at home, on my Island. I will be in touch with you and keep you posted on my trip and the decisions I make. I will be keeping a journal especially for this adventure and I will share it with you. The excitement of revisiting home, and Zan, after all these years, is beyond measure.

I am going home to my island for ten days!

Vanessa, I will send you a vacation journal 'email' each day.

Part 4

Vacation Journals

Revisiting Home—Decades Later

Dearest Vanessa,

The time is closely approaching for me to visit home and listen to my heart to see how it feels there. While I was making my plans, Zan offered me the chance to stay at his home instead of a hotel. He said his home would offer me the peace and tranquility I always strived for. I accepted his offer and felt comfortable. I have three days before my trip and I am beginning to feel excited and yet a bit nervous, I also had some questions surfacing like: What would it feel like to stay at Zan's home and to be around him? What memories could be triggered by being there? What old wounds would I be opening? What happens if all my fears about being with and around him come alive and I lose myself in a bout of resurfaced emotions?

His home is also in the same city where I lived in that invisible prison with the enemy and then left like a fugitive.

Maybe I should stay at a hotel and not at his home.

Part of me wanted to stay with him, but conflicting

thoughts were consuming me. A lot will have to do with him and how he handles me and my emotions, how that energy is directed or redirected will be very important. I need to pack and get ready for my trip. I also have a lot to do at my office before I leave.

My Vacation Starts Today

Dearest Vanessa,

In twenty-four hours, I will be at my destination. It has been an adventure planning this trip. Today I woke up at 6:00 am., feeling calm and joyful. I have been on many vacations and business trips all over the world, but going on this trip is the best feeling of anticipation I have had. I am going back to bed for a nap and some reflection and projection. I look forward to the entire journey, not just the destination. Check-in time for my flight is 6:00 pm., for a late-night flight, so there is a whole day ahead of me. I will stay in bed and sleep or daydream for a few hours to savor this blissful state. I love airports and I love looking at people and figuring out what their lives are like, some are so distinctive, and some are questionable, but I like watching them, nonetheless. My train ride to the airport was pleasant and I decided to have a good dinner—then I sat and waited for my check-in. My eyes were having a feast, and my heart was leaping for joy at what was ahead of me. If I could show how happy I was right now, I would forget my age and jump up and down.

My Flight Home

Dearest Vanessa,

The flight left on time and without any events to report. My memory went on when I left home so many years ago looking over my shoulder, sick, broken, scared, and confused. Now, I am a free woman.

Free from the hurts of the past, healed, and whole. I am free to stay at Zan's home without having to consult with a husband or wonder how it will look to anyone. I am free to make any decision, any choice I want, if my heart feels good on this trip home, I can choose to move home, if not fully then partially. This freedom has caused a welling up of joy that is unexplainable. I am loving life, I did not get what I wanted initially, but I am enjoying what I finally got. Thank you, God! You had a plan all along.

We just took off and settled to our altitude and can turn on our electronic devices. As I settled into the flight and got comfortable, the good anxiety revisited me, and I was dealing with it in a fun way. I asked myself how much freedom I really had at that moment. We are at the mercy of God because planes do not turn back, and I cannot change my mind now, not that I would.

Dinner was served at around 10:00 pm., which I thought was late, but with the anxiety I was experiencing, I decided to eat as a distraction because I was not hungry. I ordered two glasses of 'red wine' with my dinner: one for me and one for Zan. Well, that was a bad decision because as soon as the meal was over and the dishes were being picked up, terrible turbulence started, and I was in distress. My stomach felt like it would burst, and my head was spinning, I thought for a moment I might pass out. I became violently ill for the first time in decades of travel. My last time feeling ill on a plane was when I was running from life to life, since then I have never experienced any ill feeling while traveling, and I have been around the globe.

Everything that was on my stomach came up, I threw up all over myself; the blanket to keep me warm was the recipient of all that was in me from the waist up. Then I had to go to the Lube because the stuff from the waist down wanted out too. What a mess! After all that, some much-needed calm came for a while, and I was able to clean up and get a cup of ice to soothe my frazzled nerves and stomach. There were some more turbulent moments during the last half of the trip that brought me to serious praying for a settled flight; and if that was not possible, a quick, peaceful, and happy death.

After praying, I looked around at other people who were calling for help, some were crying, and some were screaming at the slightest jerk of turbulence. I prayed for them that their souls would be saved and before I knew it, I was waking up from a nap.

It was the last ninety minutes of the flight when I woke up with a calm, peaceful feeling and noticed there was a slight glimmer of light on the horizon. The sun was beginning to show its beautiful presence, and I was humbled to look at the sunrise from this altitude.

The sunrise was spectacular, the rays of colours, the dimensions of light, and the patterns of the clouds. There are no words to describe such an experience – it is worth seeing it for yourself. It is bigger than life! I basked in it and was happy that I was not sleeping through something so glorious. There was so much joy in that moment of still being alive, in what was ahead of me, and going back to a place I loved—this was extraordinary!

When I started seeing the countryside as we were getting closer to landing, I began to experience overwhelming emotions and I could not hold back the river of tears that started flowing. I cried at the memory of how I left under such unhappy circumstances, feeling like a fugitive, running from my hard reality, and yet not knowing where I was running to; but knew for sure I would never return to what I was leaving—and may not return ever. Now, here I am, returning after so many years of keeping my promise through some extremely difficult situations to never go back to that situation—life or death. I kept my promise!

There were times when everything was going wrong in my life—I was penniless with my feet on the bare pavement with cardboard stuffed in my slippers to keep my feet from being cut or bruised—and I was on the run and in hiding—and returning to the life I had looked like the answer. But through it all, I knew deep down returning was not an option.

When I came to the realization of how I kept that promise to myself, the tears continued, but with peace and calmness—my soul was refreshed. I was looking at what staying on course with God can do, I did not crack under the pressure of what was, because the injustice done against me could not be undone—so I chose to heal and grow—but I will revisit that situation from a different angle—I will face my opponent! I never thought this would happen—but I was returning to the scene of the crime. The tears flowed until the floodgates closed; they were cleansing my soul and washing away every sad remnant that may have been there.

I said a special '*thank you*' when the plane landed. While everyone was rushing to get out of their seats and grabbing their luggage, I was calm and peaceful and in no hurry. I was where I wanted to be, there was no need to rush.

I went through the usual process of entering any country and was looking at everything with eyes of love and appreciation; I felt I was hugged by the warmth of the summer breeze. Things had changed a lot, but many things remained the same. The accent of my Islanders was music to my ears, and the smiles I received were appreciated.

This is where I want to be.

As I completed the check-out process, I was looking to see if there was a sign with my name among the transportation services there to pick up passengers, not seeing my name, I kept walking, which seemed like a very long walk. But to my surprise, at the end of the line, waiting patiently with the look of love, was Zan.

He came forward and greeted me in a very nice, loving way. I started melting right there and then. I gave him a nice greeting in return. He looked the same, tall, handsome, about twenty pounds heavier, with a perfect manly structure, and the same presence I saw the first time I saw him was still there.

We got in the car, and he gave me a sweet kiss, looked me in my eyes, and said nothing, then we drove off joyously heading to his home where I was going to stay.

The lushness of everything: the plants, the palm trees, the flowers, the warmth of the summer sunshine, everything looked beautiful. The leaves danced for me—if my heart were not racing, I would hear the songs they were singing for me. I was living a dream of coming home and here I am on the soil of my birthplace and in the presence of my soulmate. What a divine moment!

After all the thinking and planning for this trip—here I am, looking and savoring everything and feeling splendid. As usual, I kept melting in Zan's company until I was a puddle of mush, a total mess. He was playing some serious love songs and dedicated a special one to me. The lyrics were: *"Girl, you mean more to me than any love I've ever known—by Lionel Richie."* That was such an emotional moment, a leftover tear flicked down my cheek. We sang along and he kept dedicating other tunes to me—we were a very happy couple in that car. All this time I was holding and romancing his hand and saying anything that came to my mind.

We stopped at a market on the way to his home to get some fruits and other stuff that I might need. I told him he had to feed me because I am a growing girl and have found lately, I really like to eat. We continued our journey while he took the time to express a thousand ways how he loves me.

We arrived at his home at about 9:00 a.m. As soon as he got my suitcase at the door, he grabbed me and hugged me in a serious manner and kissed me again and again. Then he said, "You look beautiful! Welcome home sweetheart—I am glad you are here." I held him tight and told him I was in bliss being here with him and out of my mind with joy, and this was a moment to behold!

He made breakfast and we sat and talked for a long time. After breakfast, we went to a different area of the house so I could get settled in and take a shower, which was needed. As we got to the back of his ranch-style home, he showed me some upgrades he had done, and from what I remembered it was now more beautiful than the original. There was an outside patio with lots of privacy facing a lovely, wooded area, and beyond that, a park. I told him how much I liked it and would join him in a moment. But he would not let me out of his sight; so, we ended up sitting on his bed talking about everything under the sun. I got up to leave, and he told me not to disappear. Those were his exact words. I asked, "Where would I go?" He said, "Don't leave me right this moment." I sat with him thinking of how much I wanted to be right here with him and how so many times through my struggles I wanted to be right here. I felt peace and joy in the moment just being with him. I did not want to leave him, I wanted to freshen up and get the leftover stuff from the flight off me.

I could not understand how I was feeling so perfectly comfortable in his company, and it was like there was no time or distance between us ever. I thought about all the dates my friends attempted to set me up within the last two decades that I refused; all the men who tried to talk to me that I always put down gently. No one, absolutely no one, ever held my interest in even having a conversation that would lead to a relationship. As far as I was concerned, I was finished with that side of life. I was a 'nun' in my heart, and nuns do not date. Every time I said *'no'* to a potential relationship, I was saying *'yes'* to my healing; I was keeping my personal power which I had lost in the past and I was not giving it away again.

Now, so many years since I went on my sabbatical and decades since seeing and being with Zan; I am so alive in this way . . . everything that I had put to rest is now alive in me and on the surface of my being.

Zan told me about his schedule for the next few days and how busy he was. But he would make sure I had transportation to get around and see all that I wanted and needed to see. After about an hour or so, he had to go out, so he set me up in a very nice area that was self-contained and private, where I relaxed, got my shower, and settled in on the patio. He went on his way and as he was leaving, he said, "Nothing is off limits to you, do what you want and be comfortable."

Zan came home a few hours later as I was waking up from my well-deserved nap, the sun was now beginning to set, and I wanted to bask in this moment—this was spectacular and very meaningful to me. I saw it when it came up from over the horizon at an amazing altitude to warm this beautiful day, and now I had the opportunity to see it go down from Zan's balcony.

It was picturesque; the formation of the clouds and the different array of colours were a feast for my eyes. Zan came looking for me just about that time and joined in absorbing the sunset. Nothing blocked the view of the sunset. He said, "I brought some dinner for us." That was a good thing because I was hungry.

After sunset I prepared the table for dinner, lit a candle,

poured two glasses of ‘red wine,’ we ate and had a delightful dinner.

Retiring to the patio after dinner, our hands were gently touching each other. He held my hand as if I were a child crossing the street while we talked about how much we missed each other and the rocks that were on our path. I laid my head on his strong, well-sculpted shoulder as each bird sang his own song in competition for attention. After a few moments I told him—sometimes I felt I had boulders on my path. He turned and gently kissed me on the forehead.

It was hard to take my hands off him; I massaged his shoulders and rubbed his back for a while. I missed touching him, being with him, talking to him. I did not know how much I missed him and realized that even though I was not on a sabbatical waiting for him; I was so glad I did not get involved in another relationship. I enjoyed him and I was free to do so. He did not try to force anything. I felt safe, I felt protected and perfect in his company; just the two of us, a full moon, and a full night ahead with me having feelings I have not had in decades….

We sat and relaxed to the summer evening breeze, holding hands, and hugging until I was ready to retire to bed. On my way to bed, Zan held me and was waiting for a signal . . . and in the most gentle and loving way I pulled away and went to my room, and he went to his. It was a peaceful departure from each other for the evening.

I knew he was happy that I was in the same space with him, and he did not have to feel guilty for having me there as we were both free. I knew he was ready for whichever way this went, but I was the one who had given up on this side of life, and I still had two significant things I wanted to do before thinking of going any further with Zan.

I was flooded with encouraging feelings for him but in a very calm way. I knew he was mine, and the ball was still in my court. The moment I laid eyes on him at the airport, I felt that strong positive life vibration that kept me wanting more of his company and his attention. He looked into my soul again and confirmed it when we got in the car and kissed me. The way he kissed me . . .I went to bed and did not lock my door; I was comfortable, and I did not want to act as if I was in a strange place because I was not—I was at home. In the home, I wished happiness for those it was being built for. I wished that before meeting Zan when my soul was so sad.

Now I am happy in that same home with Zan. I lay in bliss for a few moments and before long, it was morning, and the birds were in a singing competition.

I got up and went looking for him. He was lying in bed with his door ajar. I called out for him, and he answered and said, "Come in."

I went in and spoke to him for a few moments, what a wonderful feast for my eyes looking at him in bed so peaceful, so perfect, and so inviting. He gave me that look and said, "Let's go make some breakfast!" I looked at him and smiled, and, I said, "Breakfast is a good idea" . . . *and a distraction from the thoughts and feelings I had.* I sat and talked to him while he prepared breakfast, I was like a radio station that you could not turn off, just going on and on. I had so much to tell him, how do you talk about twenty-plus years in a few moments?

There was a need for me to apologize to him for leaving him the way I did; and not staying in touch for all those years— this was on the surface of my consciousness.

He was sitting next to me having breakfast, and I said, "Zan, I have something to tell you, and I need to say it now." He said, "Go ahead." And I said, "I am sorry for leaving you the way I did. I really am and I am sorry for not contacting you for all those years." He was silent for a bit and his eyes welled up, he looked at me and said, "I understood why you had to leave—and I know you suffered terribly—I forgave you totally, I really do. I am glad you are back!"

The questions had no end to what happened to his marriage because we did not talk about that until now. He said some things that made sense. He said, "I did not have anything to give, I was empty. You took all my passion for love when you left. You arouse me in a different way, you touch every fiber of my being, and the deepest parts of my soul come alive with you, no one else has been able to do that before or after our affair. I come alive with you, simple mundane things have meaning, I laugh more, and there is a joy to everything when I think of you. I choose to be a workaholic and build a career and have not focused on any serious relationships; I guess I was on my own sabbatical in a different way."

I was wondering what kind of business I could start here. How do I get a business license? Can I open a gardening center?

My questions would not stop, and he was enjoying my rambling; while I followed him around like a kid with a new toy—he was my new toy. I told him what I wanted to do for the day, and he arranged transportation for me because I did not want to drive. At that point, I left him so he could get ready for his day, and I went on the patio to meditate and set my day.

As he was leaving, he came to bid me goodbye for the day

and I said to him, “By the way, I had the best night's sleep I could remember in ages. I went to bed and did not have to worry if the doors were locked or if the windows were closed. I did not have a care in the world when I went to bed, and I liked that.” He said, “You can sleep like this every night, it’s up to you.” I said, “I know.”

My Second Day

Dearest Vanessa,

It is now twenty-four hours since I am at home and with Zan. I got up and saw him off. As I walked around the house and sat outside and listened to my heart, I felt a joy that I had not experienced since I was a child. I see the potential for me to give back in a good way, where I would be nourishing the nun in me by serving; I can work differently, I can do whatever I want to do, or I can relax and do nothing for as long as I want. Maybe a home here where I can start a garden that no one can take from me. These thoughts are adding to my joy. For the first time in my life, I feel like the world is at my feet for me to pick and choose as I wish.

I am not a victim of circumstances anymore. I will accept all these wonderful things as rewards for my sacrifices and the turmoil I endured. If all the heartaches were necessary to achieve this, then they were all worthwhile.

After breakfast and before Zan left for the day; it was still early, and I was on my way to the patio, he was behind me, he held my hand and led me to his room. I followed him without hesitation. He said, "Don't be uncomfortable, I just want to talk to you." He sat on the bed, and I sat next to him, and he said, "I am tempted to take the day off and spend it with you, would you like that?" I said, "Yes, but I want you to keep your schedule and don't worry about me, I am fine." He said, "I don't want you to feel neglected." I said, "I will not." I turned around and kissed him on the cheek, and he kissed me back, I was enjoying this, and I said to him, "I have to ask you something." He said, "Go ahead." I asked, "Is there someone special in your life?" He said, "No." I froze at that moment—and that was my ticket to go ahead and kiss him until he sizzled.

I was most comfortable in that moment and enjoyed and received his love fully. Nonetheless, there was still a small part of me that was finished with that side of life, and that small part kicked in. I felt I would be crazy again for him because from the moment I set eyes on him I realized nothing had changed in all those years. I told him I could not go further, but he kept hugging and holding me and telling me everything was fine. He said, "Rose, I want you in my life and it is up to you how you want this relationship to be. I know you had a lot of disappointments, and you told me many times you are finished with dating, romance, and marriage. But I want you, I will never hurt or disappoint you and I will settle for whatever you want for this relationship, again, it is up to you. Whatever you want is yours. I am yours if you want me." I told him, "I love this special relationship and do not want to spoil it in any way." He said, "You could not spoil this regardless of what you do, just don't leave me again, that is the only thing I can't live with." I said, "I never will."

My Third Day

Dearest Vanessa,

Today I intended to wake up before the sun to meditate. I wanted to be deep in meditation while the sun was coming up, but I missed it. When I got up the sun was already up, and I heard Zan moving around so I decided to go see his face and be around him. Zan is a bit shy and there is that way he looks at me that thrills and captivates me and I cannot get enough of it. He looked at me and asked, "Do you ever feel like you have died and gone to heaven?" I said, "Yes, I feel that way now, and have felt that way most of the time since being on my sabbatical." He said, "I am feeling that now. You are the reason I could not have anyone special in my life; because there was always the possibility of you, and unconsciously, I wanted to be free for you—just in case. The thought of you puts me in that state of bliss." I said, "You are a wonderful man, successful, appealing, and appetizing. Any woman would want you and you could probably get whatever you want." He said, "That is not the issue. The issue at hand is that true love is permanent . . . and what I have for you is permanent! I have tried to find you in other people, and they have always come up short—and with the thought of you now instead of me always thinking of my next patient and their issues which I have consumed myself with—I am now thinking about the wine supply. Is there enough wine 'that you like' in the cellar; What is for dinner; Is there enough food in the house; Where can I take you for a romantic evening; What can I do to surprise you; What can I do to make your days better and more joyful?

Through the years, I wrote you many 'love' notes on the prescription pads; there is a drawer with some of them in my office. Whenever I look at my calendar and there is any free time, I give that time to you, then sometimes the thought of you demands my time. What is happening here is a deep desire of mine to be with and around you—my wishful thinking is now my reality. When you said you were coming on this vacation, I did not sleep for many nights feeling it would not happen so, I wrote manifesting notes literally every day, and now you are here. So, now the free time on my schedule gives me an opportunity to come looking for you—just to see you is a joyful experience. My life has meaning with the thought of you. My issue is of the heart. What you are explaining about me being able to get anyone is not a reality for me—I cannot find true love anywhere—I have true love with you. What may be easy for me to get is sex." Vanessa, I know you understand this because you and I had this conversation and you told me some very similar things to what he explained.

I am going on the road today to visit some old friends and look around at some other things. It is such a beautiful adventure being here and going around the places I used to know. The driver, Mik, who is taking me around, is a good tour guide to be on an adventure with. He is about forty years old, he worked as a tour guide before and now has his own taxi service, and because of his connection with Zan, he is personally taking me around. He is teaching me things about my city I never knew. It is like a history lesson on wheels.

Revisiting the Convent

Dearest Vanessa,

I told Mik I have a special assignment for him tomorrow. I want to go to a place about an hour from Zan's home, it is a convent. When you take me there, I want to be left for an hour or so. I will be on and around the grounds so you will need to find a comfortable place to wait for me.

This is a chapter I need to close.

The next morning came, and we headed to the convent. On the way I asked Mik to drive a particular route, the same route that was planned for me when I was wounded. Mik obeyed without question. As we approached the area where the incident happened, I experienced some stirred-up emotions of anger and nervousness which eventually subsided.

We reached the convent a few miles later and as I got out of the car, I was shaking but I hid it from Mik—then I approached the grounds. I savored each step in this place I played and ran and wanted to be more than any place in the world. I stopped at the water fountain and took a drink of water then kept going. Then I sat on the first bench under a running rose harbor and looked around at some nuns on the premises going about doing their daily chores. I focused on the old connecting chapel that was opened to the public, and I decided to visit my old chapel.

As I approached the chapel my tears took on a life of their own and they flowed. I entered the chapel and walked around, it was almost empty, apart from a few people praying and a nun or two walking around. I blessed myself at the altar and fell on my knees with my face to the ground and I was there for a long time in that position. I gave everything back to God and asked that it be His will in my life. I said, "God, I did the best with what I understood, but please let me be closer to you, and from this day forth let me hear you as clear and loud as possible."

Moments later, someone handed me some tissue and held my hand to assist me off the ground. I kissed the hand that helped me and did not look up. I dried the tears from my face and moments later I got up and walked to the support box and placed a cheque in it. I left the chapel walking slowly, literally making baby steps, one foot in front of the other—I did not want to leave. My life here was cut short without my consent. I belong here. I need more of this; I would like to worship at this chapel regularly.

I walked the grounds, sometimes retracing some of the steps I remembered taking; I broke down again when I was leaving the main gate because I remembered that night; the night I left here under a stormy sky with fierce lightning and thunder as my companions. The world was sad, and I was devastated.

Today I am living under a beautiful, clear sky, and that is the way my life looks as I look ahead, beautiful, and clear—with my head up.

After My Convent Visit

Dearest Vanessa,

My thoughts today . . .

When I was planning this vacation, I wondered how I would feel seeing Zan, and how he would respond to me. I knew I would be strong and keep my promise to myself and my sabbatical, and it was not a question to even ponder. He had proven to be a good person in my corner through the years, but this was a distant relationship and not to forget, it was a very strong, life-changing love affair. I felt we would continue this wonderful friendship we had easily, but now being with him after a few days, I am excited about him all over again. And what he told me about his desire for me has caused me to feel more passion for him, he connected to my soul—this sort of absolute love and certainty comes 'once in a lifetime' for some of us—not all of us.

I think about all the friends I may have annoyed who attempted to set me up on dates and have tried counseling me about moving on and forgetting the past. All the men I have put aside with one excuse or another; not being in any situation that could cause discomfort to me, and not being out at night alone are all so different now with Zan. He broke through all those boundaries. I know for sure this is the man for me because nothing matters when I am with him. I want him, not just as a friend, but as my partner. We do not have to sleep with each other today or tomorrow. I know this is who I want to love in that special, intimate way. There is a difference between a belief and a knowing, and I know for sure—it is Zan!

My Fourth Day

Dearest Vanessa,

It came to me very clearly as I lay in bed last night; Zan and I are one, we became one the first night we consummated our affair all those years ago—and that is what caused us to never really connect with anyone else. I did not want to be in the house with that man I was married to after I met Zan, I felt I was doing Zan wrong, and I was never totally into my second marriage, I could not give my whole heart there because Zan had it—and he took good care of it.

In the middle of the afternoon, Zan came home as I was leaving to go visit an old friend. I was so excited to see him. I was ready to cancel my plans so I could spend time with him, but his maid was there, and he had scheduled an impromptu dinner for some associates that evening to be held at his home so there were lots of activities. I kept my appointment and went to see my friend. It was interesting the way he asked me where I was going and when will I be back; and if I needed anything, but what could I need?

After the party, the maid was cleaning up and I could not wait for her to leave. When she did, Zan and I retired to the patio to relax and unwind from the day. It was a hot night—and after the party and a few glasses of wine—Zan took off his shirt to cool off as we sat on the patio, and at that moment I decided to take off my top too. . .

It was so much fun looking at Zan's reaction to me being topless sitting across from him. He was totally confused. He could not remain in his seat, he was over in front of me putting his masculine hands on my breast, we were both excited, he sent trills through me that I had forgotten about. He said, "I never thought this moment would happen and God knows I prayed for it. I always loved your breasts, and I had my own relationship with them, and you took them away. Please do not ever do that again." Later he said, "Thanks for taking that top off." I relaxed and let him rekindle what belonged to him.

We lay on the patio looking at the stars cooling off in one way and getting steamed up in another. Even though I knew it was okay for us to move forward in this direction, the patio was not the place, and we were both too tired and exhausted to move. We lay there for a while until I got up and went to bed; I left him on the patio sleeping like a baby. I knew he had a very busy day which started early, and this was after midnight, this was around 2:00 a.m.

My Fifth Day

Dearest Vanessa,

Today for the third time since I have been here, which is literally every other night, I have had a recurring dream of the man I was married to attacking me in the park beyond Zan's home. In the attack, I was fighting and hitting him in the face with a large crystal vase. Each time I woke up feeling exhausted and in a panic. The first time I had the dream I was not happy about it; the second time I thought maybe because I was in the place where so much had happened and memories were resurfacing; but the third time, last night, I was uncomfortable and almost in a rage when I woke from the dream. I have never experienced a dream like this. I mentioned this to Zan as all I was doing was talking, but despite these dreams, I rested very well and peacefully in Zan's home. When Zan left for the morning and I was waiting around for my transportation, I decided that I would pay a visit to that man I was married to. I did not pass by his house since being here, I had no interest, but I am going there today, and I am hoping he is at home. This is the last hurdle I need to overcome, and I need to settle this once and for all.

My Sixth Day

Dearest Vanessa,

Facing My Opponent – The next chapter I must close…

When Mik picked me up today, I asked him to go in the direction of my opponent. The place I once resided, and the place I ran from to find myself decades ago.

As we pulled up in front of the house which looked abandoned, I thought maybe no one was residing there. The house looked unoccupied with lots of vines growing all over it. I asked Mik to go find out if Burton was there, and if so, tell him Rose wants to see him.

Mik approached the gate that was once supported by a beautiful picket fence romanced by running roses. Now it was an old, dilapidated fence that had not been maintained. At that moment, I wondered what my life would be like if I had stayed here, that thought horrified me. By this time Mik was knocking on the door. Then a very old man came to the door, I could not see clearly and thought maybe different people were occupying the house. Mik carefully descended the stairs, approached the car to my window, and said, "He is here and doesn't seem to know the name, Rose." I said to Mik, "I want you to be a witness to my conversation with this man, please come with me." Walking to that front door was like walking in a horror movie—I felt I would stumble and fall on the broken cement that was once a beautiful walkway or fall through one of the threaders on the stairs. Nonetheless, I approach gently and carefully. Approaching the door where Burton stood, I said, "Burton", he looked at me and said, "Oh! it's you, come in, please come in." I said, "I do not need to come in because I will not be long. I just want to tell you something." He said, "I have been ill for the last two weeks with the flu, and today is the first day I am up and feeling a bit better."

I was not there to chat with an old friend—because he was not.

This was my opponent—the man who ruined my life, so I immediately started talking . . .

I said, "Do you remember when I went to the convent to become a nun decades ago?" He said, "Yes, yes, I remember." I continued, "And do you remember the night you took sexual advantage of me?" Fumbling—he said, "Well . . . well—it was not like that." I asked, "Do you remember I conceived and had to leave the convent at the age of fifteen; then we got married and never consummated the marriage? And I left here after I was drastically ill, and you threatened me to come back, or I would suffer.

Well, I always wonder what the best way would be to deal with this crime you committed against me. I know the authorities here would not deal with a crime so old and I cannot have you prosecuted anywhere else; so, here is what I am demanding of you in the presence of my friend Mikel 'Mik' Jones.

My mother is traveling and will be back next week, I will not be here, but I want you to make an appointment to see her and tell her what you did to me that night on my way to the convent. I am going to have Mik who is witnessing this conversation, check back with you to be sure you do that! And then I want you to tell our child who is old enough to know the truth."

He said, "Rose, I am sorry I hurt you and wrecked your life, please forgive me. And I always wanted to give you something from our life together—I will fix that. Rose." I said, "I forgave you ages ago, and I forgive you again—right now—in this moment, and I do not want anything from our time together, you can give whatever that is to our child. May God bless you! I want my mom and our child to hear this from your own lips." He said, "Ok, ok, I will go visit your mom and tell her. I am sorry, Rose. You are a lovely girl." I said, "Thank you," and started to leave - and he added, "Rose, I am sorry, please forgive me. I have suffered terribly, and I know I need to correct this mistake. I am sorry." I looked him in the eyes and did not utter another word—Mik and I left.

I returned to the car in disbelief. This was someone who looked about twenty-plus years older than his age. For a moment I was questioning myself, was that Burton or his father? But it was him, just worn out and now recovering from the flu.

I sat in the car and exhaled and could see Mik looking at me from the rear-view mirror in quiet disbelief.

My mom visits me every year, and I meet her on some of her trips around the islands. I told her the truth about that night in question a few months ago when she visited me in London before I went on my revelation cruise; she was shocked. She held me and blessed me profusely for the pain I endured alone. She said, "You were just a child. I am sorry we did not protect you enough. I always wondered what made you consent to something like that when you had 'one vision' and I had talked to you in such detail about being careful with your life. Now I know the truth, and I believe you, I am so very sorry."

Mik and I drove in silence for a few minutes. I was in too much shock to speak—then about ten long minutes later when I exhaled again, I said, "Mik, you can talk to me and do not be uncomfortable. This is no secret anymore. That man could have ruined my life, but God did not let him succeed." Mik said, "I cannot believe what just happened. You look like only the best things have happened to you all your life, you do not look like you ever suffered in any way." Mik, "It's the grace of God you see when you look at me." That experience took the wind out of my sail, and I decided to change what I was going to do that day. I said, "Mik, take me to Dr. Zan's office. As we got there, I was lucky he was between patients and was available so, I went in and told him what I just did. He was surprised, and said, 'That was a good thing you did because if you are dreaming of being attacked by him, that is your subconscious telling you something needs to be dealt with, so it can be cleared up once and for all.'" He gently held my face, kissed me, and said, "You did the right thing, you are a woman of substance." I hugged him and left his office.

The day went very well after that confrontation; I knew that was a very important matter I had to address but was never sure how. It needed to be addressed, and today was the day. Thank you, God, for the strength you gave me to handle that situation the way I just did. I want a confession from him to my precious Mom and my child. Because they were also hurt terribly by what he did. My dad was rather forgetful now and his health was not the best, so there was no need to include him in the confession. My Mom will fill him in as she sees fit.

While driving around after addressing my opponent, I asked Mik to drive me through a lovely village on the outskirts of the island called Sand Castle's Village. I had just seen a sign pointing in its direction—saying it was another three miles to the left, and I had also read about some of the shops and restaurants in the local newspaper. It is a beachfront village with a well-maintained boardwalk. Some of the restaurants and shops are within walking distance of the ocean, a quaint-looking village with beautiful cottages and well-manicured landscapes. This looks like a very old village, but it is not. Some homes had boats on their driveways; and none of the homes had lot numbers, each had a name. The streets were cobblestone, and the streetlights were old lanterns with hanging flowering plants on every other one.

We passed a second shopping area with a few boutiques, an ice cream parlor, a beauty shop, a post office outlet, a bakery, and a few other stores. One of the boutiques was so inviting I had to stop and pay a visit. On entering, I spoke for a few moments to a friendly woman about my age and then I proceeded to look at some of the lovely items for sale. There was a rack of silk night dresses in a few choices of pastel colors, I was drawn to a short pink one, and asked for my size. It was exquisite. I made my purchase and left the store. Pink is the color for love.

We kept on our journey and soon saw a chapel with an adjoining school; this whole area was breathtaking, I felt like I had been here before. Maybe because of the photos I saw in the papers I read only recently.

About five blocks from the boutique there was a beautiful row of homes on a curved street off the ocean's path, a few of them backed up to the ocean with their own private dockyard. The last home on the end of the street was a cottage that looked very familiar with a 'for sale' sign in the front yard. I had seen a replica of this home in the countryside in London. The cottage in London was picture book pretty and I took a photo of it and had it enlarged and framed. It is above my desk in my office, I looked at it often and now I can hardly believe my eyes. I had to pinch myself.

This was a white cottage surrounded by many beautiful, running rose bushes of different colors, a few of them were romancing a harbor that was balanced by an iron rod-designed bench to the bottom. Upstairs had a private balcony. The entrance to the cottage had two oversized peace doves to welcome you in, and to the side under the upstairs balcony was a car port. The front door was a vibrant red and that was hard to take my eyes off. Then my eyes were drawn to the name written off to the side, but I could not recognize the name from the distance. I asked Mik to stop because this was a moment in time. I felt I was here before so, I inquired if he knew about this area and these homes, he said, "They were built maybe less than twenty years ago." That means they were not here when I was a little girl. I wrote down the street name and the other information that was on the 'for sale' sign, I also took a photo, and we were about to go on when I saw an older woman walking briskly towards the gate waving her hands and beckoning us to come.

Mik stopped the car, and I got out slowly looking around

to be sure I was the one being called. I walked towards this older lady who greeted me with a big smile stretched out her arm to touch my arm, and said, "How are you today?" I said, "I am fine." She said, "I saw you looking at the house and gathering information, so I hurried to reach down to you before you left, then when I got here, I felt encouraged to call you." She continued to say, "Initially, I was at the back of the house doing something and felt drawn to come to the front, then I saw you. Would you like to come in and see more of the home?" I was surprised and said a slow— "Well, yes, I would love to!" And before long I was following her around and looking at all the features of the house that kept captivating me—I fell in love with what I saw.

*I thought to myself, this is the perfect home for me. I could see myself living here, I would decorate this way and put this here and that there, and I have that perfect photo—the (almost) replica of this home from the photo I took in London—I will put it over the 'fake' fire*place...

I was daydreaming in that short space of time. Then she finally introduced herself as Mrs. Scottsdale, and I said, "I am Rose." She told me she purchased this home over fifteen years ago and loved it immensely, and now she needs to retire and move closer to her daughter and grandchildren in another town and decided to sell about six months ago and cannot find the right buyer. She shared that it is not about the money, it is about the right person who would love it as much as she did. She called it "*Joy's Nest*" and then she showed me that was the name written on the front of the house in beautiful calligraphy off to the side of the front door—which I was trying to read from the road and could not. She said, "Rose, I want to show you what I think is the most beautiful part of this home."

I followed her through her bedroom to a balcony that stretched the whole length of the back of the house to another connecting bedroom. The quick glimpse of her bedroom was spectacular, the kind of room I would like for myself. The balcony was very private, and it overlooked a beautiful landscape of flowers and well-manicured lawns. I stood there in awe, remembering Ms. Smith and her home and feeling a similar connection with Mrs. Scottsdale. This was a full circle moment thinking of Ms. Smith and how I went there as a homeless 'servant' girl who had no choices; and now I am here with Mrs. Scottsdale, a free woman, looking at things from a different level of life only because of the choices I made.

Feelings of thankfulness and joy overwhelmed me, and

Mrs. Scottsdale looked at me in that moment, and then she looked back at me again, and said, "I feel this home is right for you." My eyes were filled with tears, I was full of thankful emotions; I did not cry, there was no need to cry—those were tears of joy making an appearance. Then she proceeded to give me her direct number and insisted that I call her and not the real estate number I had copied. She asked me what was bringing me here to Sand Castle's Village. I told her I was from the Island. I grew up here in another part of the island many years ago then migrated to London for a few decades, and now I am thinking of returning. I am on vacation to see how my heart feels here. She said, "If you decide to come home, give me a call and I will work out a special deal with you. I would love to hand this home over to you." I thanked her, and she stretched her arms out to hug me, we hugged for a moment. And she said, "You have a wonderful aura about you, a Divine Spark!" I thanked her once more and asked if I could see the back garden again before I left.

Mrs. Scottsdale walked me toward the side of the house that led to the backyard where I saw the manicured lawns and flowers from the upstairs balcony; I was in disbelief at the way the garden was designed. I wanted to see the garden up close to see how much I would redesign it to my liking. But there would not be much to do with this garden, and there was space for me to add a harbor and a swing bench. Just a bit of adjusting here and there would be needed, it was a perfectly designed garden with lots of flowers and plants I liked. It looks like a garden that was designed for me. At that moment, I looked at a section of flowers and they were all facing me. I said 'Thanks' to Mrs. Scottsdale and 'thanks' to the garden, and she escorted me to the car—and I left in awe.

Mik asked, "What just happened?" I told him of my experience and what just transpired, and he said, "That is a lovely home for you—it suits you perfectly—I cannot believe what I am witnessing today." And I said, this is a divine plan!"

I went home early and was in deep thought about my visit to the enemy I once lived with; and the house that once held me enslaved to its four walls that are now just standing in disarray.

I left there earlier in the day, visited Zan, and let my intuition lead the way and it took me to see a home I would love to make my own; a home I was seeing for a second time; first in London, and now here. This must be a divine plan.

This home, and meeting Mrs. Scottsdale, captivated me and sent me into deep thought. I have just closed two old chapters on the past and now without effort, new ones are opening to me.

I poured two glasses of 'wine' and went on the patio.

My trip here has taken on a life of its own. On this trip, I have finally relinquished the idea of being a nun; and have closed the book on the night that ruined my life. Now I have a different degree of freedom and I am ready to rekindle with Zan on another level. There is now a sweet melody to my life, a sweet song. I found myself humming as I lay on Zan's patio, "Let it be, let it be, let it be, speaking words of wisdom, let it be... The Beatles."

A gentle touch on my face woke me from my nap. I was relaxing and thinking about the day and did not know I had gone off to sleep. Zan asked, "Are you okay, and why two glasses of wine?" I said, "This is a ritual of mine, I started it the day I received your first letter, and we rekindled our friendship many years ago—before my sabbatical. I would always pour two glasses every time I received your letters: one for me and one for you. When I am finished with mine, then I drink yours." He smiled and said, "You are amazing!"

This was too early for him to be home, and I asked him what brought him home at this time. He said, "I was missing you and wanted to see you."

We spent some time together and then had a snack and were necking in his room, which was a new favorite pastime of mine. We were getting cozy in the middle of the afternoon when his phone rang, and he had to leave for an emergency. As he left, I felt lost, like I used to feel decades ago, and could hardly wait to see him again. I had lots of good things scheduled to do each day on my vacation, but each time we parted I felt alone in the moment. I felt free with him, and most of all, I felt safe. And even though we did not go the extra mile last night, I am so happy I went there by exposing my breast in his presence, it was joyful watching his reaction and enjoying the way my body felt. That was a huge step in the direction my heart was leading, and he received it as I expected.

Prior to my visit, I thought I would spend some time with relatives and not be at his home every day, but now, I am not going anywhere. I will do my visits during the day, evening, lunch, dinner or what have you, but I am spending every night with him. It is an adventure for me, and I am having the time of my life. I like being around his home and confusing him, just about now he has no idea where a lot of stuff is because I have been moving things around. And I like how he is always looking for me and calling my name. His voice echoes a sweet melody to Rose—Rose, where are you, where is this, or where is that?

My Seventh Day

Dearest Vanessa,

End of My Sabbatical

I did some running around and came in to relax just after lunch. When I came home, Zan was there. I was taken aback to see him and thought maybe he just stopped by for something and would be leaving shortly. The maid was there. I went to his room looking for him and found him passed out sleeping across his bed. I left and went to the patio and saw his shoes and socks out there just thrown along with some papers he was reading. I realized he was tired. So, I got comfortable, as I had just come in myself from the day's heat and went on the patio and stretched out. After a few hours, he came and joined me and asked about my day and if I was enjoying myself. I said, "I am having the time of my life." I started playing with his feet and talking to him. I was in a very good upbeat mood, and so was he.

We watched the evening news and had dinner with the television in the background. Then he told me he had to meet a few people who were visiting from other islands. I asked him if he was coming back, and he started laughing hard. I said, "You can go anywhere as long as you come back." He came and kissed me as he was leaving and called me Rose, Rose;

we hugged, and he left. As he was leaving there was a beautiful moon on the horizon, a week less than a full moon (waning gibbous), but a beautiful moon nonetheless, and it was positioned in perfect view for me, just for me. As he walked to his car, he said, "I will be back before the moon disappears!" I said, "Don't let me come looking for you!"

I sat out until about 11:00 pm., and he was not back. The phone rang a few times, but I did not answer. After eleven thirty I went to bed and as I was falling off to a dreamy sleep, I heard him come in, but I was sleepy and halfway in a dream. He came to my room, looked over at me, and then went to his. I did not acknowledge him; I just felt him over me, and I went off to sleep and woke up at 2:30 am., overwhelmed by the thought of him in the next room, this was my seventh night, and this did not happen before.

I got up and went on my knees before God—and after praying for a long time, I took off the 'wedding band' I wore for twenty years as a promise of my celibacy, during my sabbatical and placed it on the vanity.

After closing the chapters of my life by visiting the convent; my opponent; dropping the disguises, and my healing cast; I have just given up my sabbatical and will rekindle with Zan, this is not forbidden anymore. This is our time now!

I went to his room. He was not sleeping. He looked at me and asked, “What took you so long?” I was appropriately dressed for the occasion with the lovely ‘pink silk’ night dress I bought earlier in the day . . . I crawled into bed with him, and he could not take his hands off me, and that was what I wanted.

Zan and I loved each other until the sun came up! We became one for a long time. We reconnected our souls as we did that first night decades ago. This was the wedding night I never had, there was nothing to adjust to—I was with the other half of me, the other half of my soul. I was whole again and so was Zan. We re-consummated our souls.

There is no separation of connected souls regardless of the physical distance. Zan and I never parted. We were just not in the same physical space for many years, but we never parted, and we never will.

The next morning, eight days here, I sat up in bed and looked at Zan. He said, “Good morning, sweetheart,” and I responded with a smile. Then I went to the patio to meditate. About fifteen minutes into the meditation, I opened my eyes and there were seven doves almost at an arm’s length from the end of the patio; I was in awe—I took that as a sign that our souls are sealed for the rest of our natural lives. A perfect omen!

I do not think I could feel better than this!

Zan just came to his home office dressed and ready to leave for the day. I am journaling. He came and kissed me and said he was leaving for the day and gave me that look. He walked off and then came back and hugged me lightly and asked, "Are you okay?" I said, "I have never felt better!" He smiled. And I told him I missed him already and he had not left yet. I also told him how handsome he looked this morning; he looked so happy and joyful; I could see he was in bliss—he was glowing, and he was whole again.

My Eight Day

Dearest Vanessa,

I am very, very happy that I waited and healed my broken life and am at this point now.

There is a beautiful hum again in my life...

It is a good feeling to be where you want to be in life, and not where society and other people dictate for you. I do not think I could remember feeling this loved in my life and this cared for and yet free. I do not need anything from Zan, only his love and respect. And he does not need anything from me except my love and respect in return.

My heart is happy. I have a lot to give from all those years of nurturing and healing my life. I want to give back to life—I stand before the world with a full bowl that is running over with love and good things. I am no longer standing with an empty bowl trying to have it filled by the world or relationships.

I am going to sit on the patio and savor these joyful emotions for the rest of this wonderful day. The road shall not see me today.

My Ninth Day

Dearest Vanessa,

I feel like I have known you all my life, I feel so comfortable with you. You appeared at the perfect moment when I needed an outlet; but not any outlet, one with the right moral credentials to support my situation. I thank you, and I appreciate our divine friendship.

Just now when I came to Zan's study, his doctor's coat was on the chair; the one he wore yesterday, I picked it up and smelled it, and then started laughing out real loud at how silly I am. When I was cuddling with him this morning, after creeping into his bed in the wee hours of the morning, I told him there was a 'gremlin' moving around his house and loved getting in bed with him. He said, "That my gremlin – let her have her way!"

I will not suppress any of these feelings of overwhelming joy because I know what deep indescribable sorrow is.

My happy heart is singing, and I am dancing to the tune of Zan and Rose.

I am in bliss! I am going to smell his coat again and then start getting myself ready for the day. My vacation is ending—it is time to leave . . . and I do not want to.

My Tenth Day

Dearest Vanessa,

I am finished with the road for the day, and I am relaxing and getting ready for my flight at midnight, I am also reflecting on the events of this wonderful trip—a trip of a lifetime.

This trip served many purposes. I closed the book on the unpleasant events of my life, and I ended my sabbatical.

Now I am opening a new book with my true soulmate, and I have seen enough to decide where I can open a business to serve a need in some way; there are lots of opportunities to give back and I will focus on the one that touches my heart.

My trip could not have been better, my heart is satisfied.

Departing—Leaving Zan

Dearest Vanessa,

The plane just took off and has settled to its altitude. My projection is for a calm and peaceful flight. The anxieties are different now, and I do not need to eat as a distraction; I have enough wonderful thoughts and feelings to savor. Zan took me to the airport, but before he did, we spent some private time and he stated two things very clearly: one, the ball is still in my court and, he will never move it; and two, do not leave him hanging. I said, "I am very close to making a decision and you will be the first to know, but be certain, I will not leave you again or leave you hanging."

We took off before sunrise and now the sun is up. When I boarded the plane and fastened my seat belt I exhaled, put my head back, and *'Thanked God.'* I felt Zan's spirit was on the plane with me, and I did not want to do anything to interrupt that wonderful feeling, so I kept my head back and closed my eyes.

I slept through the initial rising of the sun and looked at the formation of the clouds and the array of colors. To my surprise, there was a double rainbow, which held my breath with its beauty, and its meaning. I felt it was a sign for me.

I always heard that God gives you double rewards for your trouble, but I think he is giving me triple.

I will be home for two days before returning to work and would like us to have lunch or dinner, so call me. Oh, by the way, I did not have those haunting dreams anymore.

Thanks for being on this adventure with me.

Your friend,
Rose.

Back to My Office

Back to work with a full in-box of things waiting for me: mail to open, documents to review, things to sign; and meetings to attend—but I have a different focus. On my drive to work, I listened to an old song on the radio, the lyrics said, *"When you walk let your heart lead the way, and you'll find love every day...-Dione Warrick."* I love that. I am living that. I feel so much love in my life right now it is unbelievable.

I went from victim to victorious by choosing excellence!

Today I am having lunch with Vanessa, and I can hardly wait to see her.

I ran around all morning getting things done while keeping an eye on the time to meet Vanessa. At 11:00 a.m., she called and said it would be best to meet at my office and I agreed. As she arrived, I said before we left, I must show you something. I said, "Remember the house I told you about on my vacation, Mrs. Scottsdale's home." She said, "Yes." I said, "This is the house!" I saw it in the countryside in London many years ago and felt a connection to it then; and when I saw it on my vacation a week ago, I knew that was God's plan, and I made a good connection with the owner, Mrs. Scottsdale. Vanessa could not say anything, she just shook her head.

At the restaurant, we ordered two glasses of 'red wine' to celebrate the journey. After I had my first sip, my phone rang. I answered the phone, and it was Mik, the driver, my new friend from back home. He said, "I need to let you know that I just came from witnessing Burton's confession to your mother about what he did to you that horrible night while you were attending the convent. Burton was shaking profusely, and your mother cried." She said to him, "You could have killed my child, but God took care of her, and no one knew the pain she suffered in silence." He went on to say, "Burton apologized generously to your mom and asked for her forgiveness. And promised that he will be having the same discussion with his child the next time they are together." Your Mom told him she forgave him.

Vanessa and I had a wonderful lunch and rekindled a lot of my journey that I was not able to journal, she confessed that she is not living her passion and my life has taught her a great lesson—she needs to live her passion and she needs to start living it now!

Part 5

Returning to Love and a New Life

The bitter, the sweet, and the tasteless of life have consumed me; my choices to stay on the narrow path have brought me out on this side of life and I am making steps in the direction of continued choices for excellence.

After my journey of struggles, and life's ups and downs, I am thinking of the decision that is in front of me, I want to live differently—I want to return to love.

I had to make that trip. And I am so happy about the time I spent with Zan because I want him in my life. I am not sure if I want to marry again, but I know I want him as my significant other, my life's partner—we will figure that out.

It is very important that I maintain my dream of having a place of my own; it could be in the country—a place for us to visit on weekends, or a place for me to spend time and keep nourishing me when I am not running Zan down. I love my home Island, and I saw many ways to live and serve there. I can have a great church life and give to my convent and be a volunteer in any way needed. My convent and chapel hold my roots; I want to be part of that but now in a different way. I will create new ways of giving. I do not need much, so I know what to do with the rest of what I have accumulated. And I want to worship at my old chapel.

How often do people get a second chance at a first love? Also, Zan and I are middle-aged now, so if not now, when? Why would I not go back to him now? Life is short, and we all need to love and be loved.

Without true love we are just breathing in and out, just existing. Until you find the love that makes you smile from deep inside, you do not know what joy is.

I have found the love I missed for many years of my life. I cannot leave it again. I have nothing to run from; I have everything to run to. I am going back to my homeland and to Zan.

It seems I was not worthy of being a nun. Nuns are not supposed to end up pregnant. Life prevented me from my passion. This shows that negative forces and the devil can sometimes get its way. And from that experience, and the broken trust from my second marriage, I always kept myself away from any possibility of being exposed to trusting the opposite sex, or the wrong people. It was a very isolated life. But a joyful life because I live as a nun on my terms.

After the traumatic events of my life, and especially after my second marriage ended, I made a conscious decision to live and exist as a nun, and I did that for more than twenty years. I lived in private seclusion. A pure life, the life I wanted to live as a young teenager in convent.

Truly finding your destiny may disappoint those who had or wanted you to be appointed to theirs. Like all the friends who could not accept me not dating, and all the men to whom I had to tell untruths to keep them away. I was on a mission, I had to find myself.

I am a presence for God in the world, just in a different way. My life draws good people and good situations to me. I think the pureness of my heart shows on the outside because of the way people respond to me. Men are all around me in the most respectful ways, trying to carry my bags and opening doors for me, my male neighbors fight to see who would be first to clear the snow off my driveway or cut the few feet of grass. I really appreciate my life and the love I find everywhere.

Children and babies gravitate towards me in warm ways. I lived alone and secluded by choice, but I was never lonely. I refused to settle for anything that was not the best for me, yet I have love in my life.

Turning back the pages of my life, I realized I did things in a big way; it was all or nothing!

When Zan came back into my life after I separated from my second husband; I was tempted to go visit him and rekindle our relationship, but that still small voice within said 'no.'

It said, "you are broken and need to heal. You might need more from Zan than he could give, and you could risk having another broken relationship—for which you cannot afford."

Everything in me was saying 'yes' to Zan at that time, but I had to decline and live through the pain.

I found comfort in my 'turtle's shell' because I invited God in, and the pain of my life started to lessen and evaporate until I was finally free of pain. If I had visited Zan when I was so broken, we may not be where we are now.

After my love for God, and my love for being a nun, Zan is the next love of my life.

Looking at the whole picture—I can see that God had a plan! He knew I wanted to be a presence in the world to represent him and he finally allowed me that.

Vanessa, I told you I am a nun, but now you know my story; I am a regular woman, who wanted to be a nun, and because of an unfortunate situation, that dream was killed, and I lost myself in the years that followed; but I never lost my trust in God, and my desire to be a nun.

Nuns are not born, they are made. I was not made into one, but I am one in my heart. I feel God's presence all the time, and His grace is sufficient.

It is not where you are ordained, or if you are ordained; it is not the clothes you wear or do not wear; the title you have or do not have. What matters is the personal power that only comes from God and that peace that surpasses all human understanding.

Through the turmoil, and twists and turns of my life, I chose excellence in the face of adversity, I stood with God's grace and the choice for peace, healing the past, forgiving, and moving forward. My choices led to freedom and unspeakable joy. In this freedom, I am properly positioned to make the choice to return to my home island, and to my love.

Since I did not get my first love to be a nun, I am settling for my second love, Zan.

I am returning to love - where I belong.

After all the lost dreams, broken promises, crossroads, and goals not met, I now have one goal: happiness. I choose happiness. And I am happy!

The End

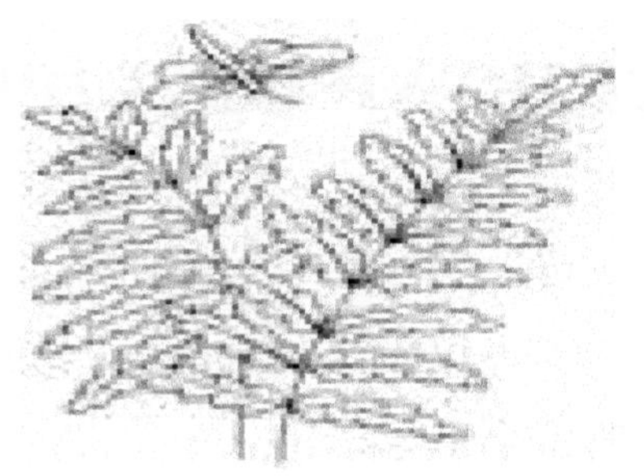

Acknowledgements

First and foremost, I give heartfelt thanks, honour and praise to God for keeping his hands on my life and for guiding and loving me. Thank you, my precious God!

Thank you, Damani Roger, my son, you showed up to teach me patience and unconditional love.

Thanks to my dad, Reginald Ramsay, and my siblings: Robert, Barbara, Linda, Brian, Jacqueline, Donna, and Deborah; and to all my nieces and nephews and their offspring.

Thanks to my aunt, Winifred Maynard, and her children: Peggy, Frank, Judy, and Roxanne; and my uncle, Ovid Hardy.

Thank you, Cheryl Brown, (Ms. Brown) you stayed with me relentlessly to make this book a reality. To you—here it is!

Thanks to Joseph Harmon, Eugene Gilbert, Patricia Prescod, Loretta St. John, Ronald Anderson, Dr. Patrick Gordon, Marva Jacobs, Colleen Forde, and Beverly Burns, my forever friends.

To everyone mentioned here—you have assisted and encouraged me in bringing this book to completion, directly and indirectly.

A sincere ‘Thank You’ to each of you!

About me

Writing is my passion. I love to write!

I have been writing for many years, but never published any of my works until 2010 when I published this novel, *I Said, "I Am A Nun"*.

It is my optimum expectation that my writing brings joy to you 'the reader' as much as it brings joy to me when I write.

Born in British Guiana (now Guyana), South America, I migrated to the USA where I have lived most of my adult life; between New York, Dallas, and now the Baltimore/Towson area in Maryland.

As am adult, I returned to college and obtained an interdisciplinary bachelor's degree in communication and human development from the Empire State College, New York. When I am not writing, I am reading, gardening, sewing, or doing some photography.

Book Reviews

By mschase on May 8, 2012

Format: Paperback

I said "I Am A Nun" will give readers the motivation and courage to get through some of the difficult situations we face every day. The author provides her readers a road map to follow, when trying to visualize the light at the end of the tunnel. The story seen through the eyes of the main character, Rose, will take you on an emotional roller-coaster ride as the author

***

"Susan Couto" <scouto@dia.ca> 01/18/2011 08:28 AM

To <juneayasmar@att.net>

SubjectI Said "I Am A Nun"

Hi June,
I am truly passionate about books; reading is my favorite thing to do without a doubt. It usually takes me to places that I have never imagined and almost always broadens my mind in ways that enhance my thoughts and believes. Your book did that! Although, I am a practicing Catholic and am blessed with a very strong faith I have never met anyone who has wanted to be a nun, therefore, found this book intriguing.
I wanted to post my feedback on Amazon, but I'm not sure if it's because your book is not yet available there, every time I tried it rejected. I did not try posting on B&N as I do not have an account with them. I am enclosing my comment for your review, or in case you would like to post it yourself.
Regards,
Susan

***

By Cforde@tumbalina

I enjoyed this book tremendously! It was fantastic! Rose kept me wanting to read on and on, she is full of love and an amazing woman. Only a few nights ago after settling down from a long day I felt like I wanted to snuggle up in bed with a good read. I thought about what it would be and "I said, I am a Nun" - my second read. I am looking forward to your next book. A big thank you June.

***

By Jacqueline Ramesar on February 12, 2013

Format: Paperback

This is a great read. I was very impress for a first time writer, this was very enlightening. I cannot wait to read June A Ramsay next Book Congratulations!

***

By mschase on May 8, 2012

Format: Paperback

I said "I Am A Nun" will give readers the motivation and courage to get through some of the difficult situations we face every day. The author provides her readers a road map to follow, when trying to visualize the light at the end of the tunnel. The story seen through the eyes of the main character, Rose, will take you on an emotional roller-coaster ride as the author

***

EVW_BSHSI

☆☆☆☆☆5 out of 5 stars.

·An Innocent Love Story....

Beautiful, innocent, passionate story!

Shrron Spencer

☆☆☆☆☆5 out of 5 stars.

Electifying: Highly Recommended: Extremely Engaging

Fantastic! A page turner. It is unbelievable what this young girl went through and yet kept her courage to keep moving forward in life. Life would beat her down and she kept coming getting up. If this book don't bring you to tears, I don't know what will. It will make you refocus on your life and your lost dreams and your passions; and puts you in a frame of mind to start fixing and rearranging things to move in the direction you were meant to go in. It makes you want to stop settling for less and to stand firm for what you want; it makes you want to make your life better and to hold on to your own dreams and passions. Taking one page from Rose's life would have you move your life in a direction or your dreams, the direction it was meant to go in. Follow your dream regardless of the bumps on the road. An extraordinary love story!

***

Shirley McKenzie

☆☆☆☆☆5 out of 5 stars.

Highly Recommended

"I Said, I Am A Nun" is an immensely well-written story of faith, courage and love of a young girl named Rose whose choices were stripped due to a shameful incident. You will be totally engaged as you journey through Rose's maturity as she discovers how to rely on herself and forgive her perpetuator. Although Rose's preferred way of life is forever altered, her resolve to continue to live in this faith never changes. You will be amazed by Rose's devotion to maintain this standard of living as she balances it with a relationship with the man who is her soulmate. This read is a delight until the very end!!

***

Review of I Said, "I Am A Nun"

Post by Jerry Spencer » 07 Apr 2023, 01:12

[Following is an official Online Book Club review of "I Said, "I Am A Nun"" by June A Ramsay.]

5 out of 5 stars

Share This Review

Julia and Rose have been best friends since childhood, and they shared a dream until Rose lost her focus. *I Said, "I Am A Nun": Choosing excellence in the face of adversity* is a romantic confession about Rose after she left the convent because she was pregnant. Julia and Rose had been dreaming of being nuns since they were seven. They'd imagine helping others and serving the Lord with their body and soul. They were both happy when they got to join the convent, but after some time, things began happening to Rose until she could no longer become a nun.

Rose was just 14 years old when she got pregnant. She felt sad and rejected. People used her as a bad example. She had to stay indoors in her parent's house. To make things worse, she had a painful, uncomfortable, and immature birth. In this book, Julia, who is still a nun, tells this story. She tells this story to Vanessa, an elegant woman in her fifties whom she newly meets. She feels she can trust this woman to lift the burden she has been carrying. Who is Venessa? How does Rose's and Julia's story continue?

I Said, "I Am A Nun": Choosing excellence in the face of adversity is written in 5 parts, which consist of 26 chapters and about 170 pages. The author of this book is June A. Ramsay. She put a lot of work into perfecting the story. A reader will have mixed feelings about this story, the beginning is sad because Rose feels she's lost everything, but as we read on, there's joy. We'd have to understand that Rose went through a lot of weakness and pain. Along the way, we uncover the truth of her pregnancy and learn of a new character, Zan, who truly makes her happy. According to her, their souls connect. Sadly, her great joy does not come without complications.

Retrospectively, we can't blame the characters for some of their actions. They were only acting in the continuum of the mistakes they had made. This book contains an adulterous romance. Focusing on accuracy, *I Said, "I Am A Nun": Choosing excellence in the face of adversity* is professionally edited.

I rate this book **five out of five stars.** I learned two primary things from this book. Firstly, we must focus on our goals unless we may end up incomplete. Secondly, we should learn to put ourselves first so we do not damage others. I recommend this book to emotionally-drained individuals, nuns, and lovers of tragedies.

***

I Said, "I Am A Nun"

Milton Keynes UK
Ingram Content Group UK Ltd.
UKHW020246221123
432980UK00016B/940